Introductory Mathematical Modeling

A first course

Authored by
Dr. Lucas Castle
Dr. Katherine Crowley
Dr. Gregory Hartman
Dr. Meagan Herald
Dr. Jessica Libertini
Dr. Troy Siemers
Mr. John Vosburgh

with contributions by
Ms. Kaylyn Kates

Contents

Chapter 1

The Process and Essential Tools of Mathematical Modeling

1.1 What is this course? (And how to succeed.)

We have questions.

Most people acknowledge the usefulness of mathematics, recognizing that without math, we wouldn't have long bridges, tall buildings, cellphones, video games, long–range weather forecasts, etc. But most people view themselves as being on the receiving end of other people's mathematical skill, and would agree with a statement like "I'm glad other people know how to do math, but I don't need to know much math myself." One of the goals of this text is to show you that even if you are not an engineer or scientist, there is likely a significant amount of mathematics that is relevant and useful to your life. Below are a few scenarios and questions that we'll learn how to answer. You will see that some are *important* questions, and hopefully you'll find most of them *interesting*.

- Michelle and her daughter Sydney enjoy playing the video game Splatoon® together, where the computer places them in a game with 6 other players and creates two teams of four. Sydney feels that she is not on the same team as Michelle more times than she is. How can she tell if the computer is keeping them apart?

- You work for a national park, and you have visitor data for the last five years. What is a meaningful prediction about the number of visitors to your park this year?

- Think of two athletes from two different sports. Can you make a case for why one is a better athlete than the other? (If one can answer this question, one can make lists like ESPN's "Top North American Athletes of the Century.")

- A friend tells you a gas additive will give you better gas mileage. You try it and for one tank of gas, you do seem to get better mileage. How can you tell if it is from the additive, or some other factor?

- Adam decides to run in a 5K as part of a fundraiser, even though he isn't much of a runner. Only a few people compete in his category, and he easily wins 1st place. A friend tells him his running time is "actually really good." What does that mean?

- During the COVID-19 pandemic, many measures were put into place to slow the spread of the virus: mask wearing, social distancing, shelter in place orders, forced closure of some businesses, quarantining, etc. Which combination of policies is best, taking into account both health and economic consequences?

- Kaylyn gets her first job after college and begins saving for retirement. Instead of saving, her friends say she should use that money for a few years so she can buy a nicer car. They reason that she'll only be able to save a few thousand dollars anyway, and that won't make much of a difference 40 years later. Kaylyn says her savings will make a BIG difference. Is she right?

Learning new things.

You aren't expected to know how to answer any of the above questions, though you probably came up with tentative answers for some of them. That's ok; this course is designed to teach you how to answer those questions, so you aren't expected to already know the relevant concepts. In fact, you may be reading this text *because* you want to learn how to answer questions like those.

With the expectation that you are reading this text with the intent to learn, it is worth reflecting on the learning process. Answer the following questions:

1. Think of a skill you possess. How did you learn this skill?

2. What would happen if you don't use that skill for a long period of time?

3. Twenty years from now, do you expect to still have this skill? Why?

Regardless of the skill you thought of, you probably became skilled through practice/repetition, and you maintain that skill through repeated use. Several of the authors of this text can play the piano. They developed this skill through hours of practice, and maintain their ability by playing on a regular basis. If they continue to play the piano, 20 years from now each author will still be able to play. If they were to stop playing now, 20 years from now they would likely recall *something* about the playing the piano, though they would have lost much of their skill. You probably recognize that you will keep your skill far into the future if you continue to use that skill, and you'll lose much of your skill without use.

The same principles apply to learning and using mathematics. You'll learn the important skills of this course through practice, and this text is designed to provide that practice. Because practice is so important, most questions in this text have an answer in the back: practice isn't very useful if you don't know if you are getting it right.

Will you retain the all skills taught in this course 20 years from now? *Not likely.* You may use some skills on a regular basis, and hence you will retain those. A goal for this course is *not* that you'll be able to retain all skills for a long period of time. Rather, our expectation is this: 20 years from now, when a situation arises that could benefit from one of the skills taught in this text, you will 1) remember that you once knew how to answer the question, 2) have confidence that you could relearn the skill, and 3) know that there are others who can help you answer the question, even if you don't personally relearn the skill.

What is this course about?

In short, *Mathematical Modeling*. That term is loaded with meaning, and we'll partially define it through an analogy. You have probably seen a *model car* at some point in time. A model car looks like a version of a real car, and one can study the model car (by, for instance putting it in a wind tunnel) to understand how the real car may behave.

A *mathematical model* is a mathematical representation of a real phenomena. (That phenomena may be how Michelle and Sydney are/aren't put on the same team; it may be attendance at a national park; it may be the growth of money in a retirement account.) We can learn about the real phenomena by looking at the mathematical model. The model may be a single number; it may be an equation; it may be a spreadsheet in Excel; it may be something else entirely.

At it's core, mathematical modeling is about understanding *real* things and solving *real* problems. It is the hope of the authors that you'll find the situations and problems presented in this course to be real, relevant, and interesting.

1.2 The Cultural Trip

Learning about other civilizations and cultures is a valuable component of a college education. Suppose a donor is willing to cover the expenses for some students to take a cultural trip, such as a semester or summer abroad. To be considered for funding, the donor asks you to present a proposal that makes a compelling case for a meaningful cultural experience worthy of college credit and includes a reasonable and organized budget. The donor also asks you to design the trip to accommodate up to 20 cadets.

Planning your Trip

Consider the following as you plan your trip:

1. Where do you want to go for your cultural trip? The only requirement is to choose a destination where the currency is not tied to the US Dollar. That is, the exchange rate is not 1:1.

2. What is the currency conversion rate between the US dollar and the currency of your destination?

3. How long will you be abroad? Is this a semester abroad or a summer trip or something else?

4. What activities and events will you participate in during your trip to build a cultural experience?

5. How much time does each activity and event take? How much does each cost? Be sure to calculate cost both in U.S. dollars and in the local currency.

6. The State Department maintains a list of reasonable per diem (per day) costs for meals and lodging abroad. You can find this State Department website by searching *foreign per diem*. Your plans might cost more or less than these per diem costs, and that is ok. Do you have any costs that will far exceed the State Department's per diem guide? Is there a good justification for keeping these in your plans?

7. What is the average daytime high/low temperature of your destination during the time in which you will be there? Do you have appropriate clothing, or do you need to purchase some before you go?

8. What other costs should you consider?

9. Make an organized budget with all of your expenses in an Excel spreadsheet.

Assignment: Cultural Trip Proposal

Part 1: Write a proposal to fund a cultural trip overseas that includes your answers to the question above. Include:

- a summary of the trip activities and goals and their educational and cultural value

- an itemized budget of activities and their costs using Excel

- at least 15 activities and their costs

- an explanation of which costs you'll pay in USD and which you'll pay in local currency, including the amount you will need converted into the local currency

- the total cost of the trip in USD

- the ability to change the number of cadets in the Excel spreadsheet who will be on the trip

- a justification for the budget

Part 2: The travel company helping book your trip adds a $200 flat reservation fee for their services charged on top of the costs for your trip. The term *flat reservation fee* means that no matter the size of the group, the fee is $200. If 5 people go on the trip, each will pay $40 toward the fee; if the group has 20 people, each will pay $10 toward the fee.

Use this information to create a table and graph showing the cost per person in USD for groups of 1 to 20 travelers. While this table and graph are not part of the official cultural trip proposal presented to the donor, you may include them below your proposal's budget table.

The donor will assess the proposal based on:

1. whether you make a compelling case for why the experience will fulfill the educational requirement;

2. whether the budget is clear, correct, and reasonable; and

3. the clarity of your presentation of the proposal.

1.3 The Cultural Trip: the Power of Spreadsheets

You will use the partially populated `CT_TripExpenses` sheet in the `MtM_Unit1_CourseContent.xlsx` workbook to answer the following questions about an international trip.

Using Formulas - The Basics

1. Type each of the following into any empty cell of the spreadsheet. What is the exact answer that you get?

    (a) $= 13 * 150$

    (b) $= B2 * B10$

    (c) $= B1 * B2 * B10$

    (d) $13 * 150$ (*Hint:* How does this one differ from the others?)

2. In the previous problem, what does each formula calculate?

Problem 1 teaches us that the equals sign tells Excel you want it to perform a calculation. We also see that answers to calculations appear in cells, while formulas appear above in the formula bar.

3. Use what you just learned about Excel to enter the appropriate formula into cell B11.
   (*Hint:* Consider what is written in cell A11.)

4. Notice that in 1(a) we entered numbers, while in 1(b) and (c) we referenced cells in the table. If we want to calculate the total cost of food, which do you think is better:

$$= 13 * 150 \qquad \text{or} \qquad = B1 * B8?$$

Multiple choice:

   (a) $= 13 * 150$ because this shows the exact number of people and the exact cost of food per person

   (b) $= B1 * B8$ because the number of people and cost of food per person might change as plans evolve

   (c) $= 13 * 150$ so we don't lose track of the numbers we're calculating with

   (d) $= B1 * B8$ because it feels fancier

Now that we have seen how formulas work in Excel, let's try writing our own.

5. In the space here, and also in cell C6, write the formula that would give the airfare per person in foreign currency.

6. In the space here, and also in cell C9, write the formula that would give the insurance per person in foreign currency.

7. What stayed the same in the two previous answers? What is the pattern?
   Multiple choice:

   (a) B2 is in both answers because we are calculating total costs based on per person costs.

   (b) B2 is in both answers because everything is calculated per person.

   (c) B2 is in both answers because the conversion rate is required for both.

Relative References

Excel is aware of the pattern too. When copying and pasting a formula, by default, Excel only looks at the relative position of the inputs. Let's look at an example.
   Enter this into cell D8:

$$= 13 * B8$$

Now copy/paste cell D8 into cell D9.
   (*Copy/Paste Hints: To copy and paste on a PC, click on cell D8 and do Ctrl+C, then click on D9 and do Ctrl+V. To copy and paste on a Mac, click on cell D8 and do Cmd+C, then click on cell D9 and do Cmd+V.*)

8. What formula now appears in the formula bar when you select cell D9?

9. What general rule can we conclude about Excel based on what happened in the previous problem?
   Multiple choice:

   (a) When you copy and paste a formula in Excel, cell references change according to the new row or column.

   (b) When you copy and paste a formula in Excel, you get an error.

   (c) When you copy and paste a formula in Excel, the numeric answer from the previous cell is repeated in the new cell.

10. Based on your answer to the last question, what do you expect will happen if you copy cell D9 and paste it into cell F15?

   (*Hint:* Notice that cell D15, which is two cells to the left of F15, is empty. What number value do you think an empty cell has?)

11. Test the guess you made in the previous problem. Were you correct?

So far we have been using formulas of the type

$$= 13 * B9.$$

In this case, B9 is a *relative reference* because when the formula is copied and pasted, B9 will change according to the new row and column.

Absolute References

12. (a) What is in the formula box for cell C6? (*Hint:* Look at your answer to Problem 5.)

    (b) What is in the formula box for cell C8, which was already filled in when you opened the spreadsheet?

    (c) What is in the formula box for cell C9? (*Hint:* Look at your answer to Problem 6.)

13. What is different about the symbols in part (b) of the previous problem, compared to parts (a) and (c)? Do an internet search to confirm or refute your guesses about what the symbols do.

It can be helpful that Excel defaults to relative position, though note that here we want to use cell B2, the currency conversion rate, in every calculation. We accomplish this by using the *absolute reference* $B$2.

Dragging Formulas

Suppose you would like to fill an entire column with a copied formula. Rather than copy and paste each cell individually, Excel has a drag feature that allows you to fill the entire column with one step as if you had copied and pasted each cell.

14. Do an internet search to learn how to drag a formula in Excel. How do you do it?

15. Use your answer in the previous problem to drag the formula in cell C7 to fill in cells C8 and C9. Which cells changed and how?

16. Move to Table B in the spreadsheet, and fill in cells B15-18 and C15-18 using relative and absolute references where appropriate. Try to write one equation per column and drag it down the column instead of writing individual equations for each cell.

Built-in Functions

In addition to basic arithmetic operations, Excel has built-in functions, including one that allows us to add up a lot of numbers quickly. If we want to calculate the total cost of the trip, it would be helpful if we could add the airfare, lodging, food, and insurance costs in one step.

17. Do an internet search or use the Excel help files to see what the SUM command does. Then use the SUM command to fill in cells B19, C10, C11, and C19.

Note that, with the SUM command, we can add more rows later for other costs such as museum fees or transportation, and rely on the existing formula to recalculate the total cost.

18. Write equations that calculate the percentages in Table C. Use relative and absolute references and drag formulas where appropriate.

Visualizing Spreadsheet Data

You can also use Excel to create graphs to visualize data.

19. Create a bar graph, a line graph, and a pie graph to help visualize the data from Table C. Which graph is best suited to displaying this type of data? Why? Are any of these graphs particularly unhelpful in this context? Which and why?

Review and Reflect

Take a moment to think back on this section. What were the main ideas? What did you find most interesting?

-

-

-

-

-

Cultural Trip Summary

In the course of planning our cultural trip, we have begun to learn how Excel spreadsheets work. We can use spreadsheets to organize data into tables, perform calculations on the data, and graph the data.

- Excel *formulas* always begin with an equals sign, the signal to Excel to do a calculation.

- When copied and pasted, *relative references* to a cell change according to the position of the new cell, while *absolute references* to a cell continue to refer to the original cell.

    - Using something like "B4" in a cell is a relative reference.

    - Using something like "$B$4" in a cell is an absolute reference.

- Formulas can be dragged to an entire column instead of copying and pasting the formula into each cell individually.

- Excel has many *built-in functions*, available under the Formulas tab.

- Most spreadsheets function in a manner very similar to Excel. As spreadsheets are very powerful and useful, there is a wealth of information about them online. You can find a solution to just about any problem you encounter through an internet search.

Exercises 1.3

Exercises 1 – 6 contain simple activities that will help you use Excel more effectively.

1. Quickly make a column of the numbers 1 through 100: enter "1" into a cell, then "2" into the cell below it. Highlight the two cells, then "click-and-drag" down. You should see numbers created in the cells below.

2. Quickly make a column of numbers *counting down* from 100 to 1.

3. Quickly make a column of the numbers 5 through 100, counting by 5's.

4. Make a column of 10 numbers, in no particular order. Then use Excel to put them in order, from smallest to largest.

5. Enter a date into Excel, such as "March 14, 2015."

   - What happens when you press Enter?
   - What happens when you click/drag that cell down?
   - Use a formula in an adjacent cell to give the day of the week of your date. (For instance, March 14, 2015 is a Saturday.)

6. Joyce manages volunteer help on Saturdays for a local charity. She wants a column of the dates for just the Saturdays of 2022. How can she quickly make that column?

Exercises 7 – 11 use the CT_TripExpenses worksheet in the MtM_Unit1_CourseContent.xlsx workbook, which you should have filled out while completing this section's activities. An image of the properly filled out spreadsheet has been provided below so you may check your work. You will need your Excel file to answer some of the questions below.

Group Size:	13	
Conversion Rate= 1USD :	¥3.725	

Table A: Breakdown of cost by person

Expenses	USD	Foreign Currency
Airfare per person	$375.00	¥1,396.88
Lodging per person	$125.00	¥465.63
Food per person	$150.00	¥558.75
Insurance per person	$100.00	¥372.50
Cost per person	**$750.00**	**$2,793.75**
Total Group Cost	**$9,750.00**	**¥36,318.75**

Table B: Breakdown of cost by expense category

	USD	Foreign Currency
Total airfare cost	$4,875.00	¥18,159.38
Total lodging cost	$1,625.00	¥6,053.13
Total food cost	$1,950.00	¥7,263.75
Total insurance	$1,300.00	¥4,842.50
Total Group Cost	**$9,750.00**	**¥36,318.75**

Table C: Allocation of funds in %

Airfare	50.00%
Lodging	16.67%
Food	20.00%
Insurance	13.33%

7. Without updating the spreadsheet and just thinking about it, consider the following: if the airfare per person is increased to $450 USD and everything else stays the same, does the percentage of total food costs for the trip increase, decrease, or stay at 20%?

8. Now update your spreadsheet to show the increase in airfare per person to $450 USD. What is the new percentage of total food costs?

   (a) about 15%

   (b) about 18%

   (c) stayed at 20%

   (d) about 21%

9. With this new airfare of $450 USD per person, what is the amount of the new total airfare cost (for the entire group) in the foreign currency?

10. Without updating the spreadsheet and just thinking about it, consider the situation where one or more people join the trip. Do you expect the percentage of the total food cost for the trip to increase, decrease, or stay the same?

11. Update your spreadsheet by increasing the group size to 14 (with the airfare at $450, as set in Exercise 8). List the new percentage for the total food cost.

Exercises 12 – 14 describe an activity given in MA101_ExtraPractice.xlsx. **Each activity gives practice using formulas and illustrates how good formatting makes a spreadsheet more understandable and usable. Sample solutions are also given in the Excel file.**

12. The sheet CT_Gradebook_Problem describes the requirements of a gradebook for a college course. (The created gradebook could be used to compute your own course grades.)

13. The sheet CT_Kitchen_Problem lists costs associated with a home remodeling project. Correctly estimating and counting the costs of materials and labor helps one properly plan such a project.

14. The sheet CT_Shopping_Problem has one calculate the cost of a small grocery shopping trip, including the tax only on items that are taxable.

Chapter 2

Modeling Data with Trendlines

Look at the four graphs shown in Figure 2.0.1, where the x- and y-axes are purposefully unlabeled. Which of the four graphs, if any, shows a discernible pattern or trend? Where a pattern exists, can you describe it succinctly?

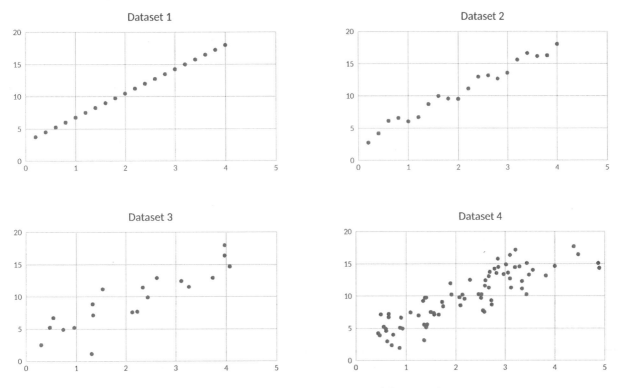

Figure 2.0.1: Identifying which datasets exhibit a trend.

Most people would agree that Datasets 1 and 2 show a pattern, though one might not be able to describe the patterns *succinctly*. One of the main goals of this chapter is to show how even Datasets 3 and 4 exhibit trends, and we'll provide a way of communicating these trends to others.

We'll learn the language of *trendlines* and use them to describe patterns in data we generate ourselves, and also in data collected from a wide variety of sources: historical populations, Netflix revenue, size of deer, numbers of visitors to national parks, number of cars shipped by Tesla, mile-run times, and more.

2.1   Modeling with Linear Trendlines

Part 1: Background

There are many reasons, big and small, that motivate people to move from one location to another. Some are fun and exciting, like starting one's first job after college or getting married and beginning a new chapter in life. Some are intended to be temporary, such as moving to a new city, state or country seeking a good education. Other moves are made in desperation, perhaps suddenly, as people flee hunger, persecution, or environmental catastrophe.

Government officials are very interested in studying the factors that lead to immigration and emigration, and policy makers use complicated models to predict the numbers of people who seek to enter and leave their country. While these models are too complicated for us to consider here, there are basic principles of modeling we can learn through the context of immigration and emigration. In this section, we will use M&M® candies to simulate immigration and emigration, then develop mathematical models to describe the observed behavior.

This section isn't really about immigration and emigration. Rather, it is about mathematical modeling. We will find equations (models) that provide insight into observed behavior even though the models don't exactly describe what is observed.

Part 2: Creating Data for Analysis

When people immigrate and emigrate, there is often a constant and predictable demand for how many people attempt to do so, and also how many succeed. For example, about 800,000 Canadians immigrate to the United States every year. Presumably, some slightly larger number attempts to each year. In this scenario, every year is a new "iteration," though "each iteration" could also mean each month, each day, or some other unit of time.

We will use M&Ms to simulate this type of data. We will start with a collection of M&Ms that represent people, and "roll" some of them. An M&M that lands with its "m" up represents a person who succeeds in immigrating or emigrating. (Don't use any yellow M&Ms because it's sometimes hard to read the "m" on them. If you have any, you can eat them before you start.)

The following table contains eight scenarios, four for emigration and four for immigration. We will do an example of each case.

Group	Type of Population Change	Starting Population	Emigration/Immigration Attempts per Iteration
Orange	Emigration	60	10
Mint	Emigration	45	6
Green	Emigration	60	6
Purple	Emigration	45	10
Blue	Immigration	8	10
Yellow	Immigration	4	6
Red	Immigration	4	10
Pink	Immigration	8	6

Simulating Emigration

We will do the Orange group example and simulate emigration data where the starting population is 60 people, and 10 people try to emigrate in each iteration. Start with three cups: one cup marked "Population" that contains the orange group starting population of 60 M&Ms; one cup marked "Roll" that you will use to roll a few M&Ms at a time from the Population cup; and one cup marked "Emigrated" to hold the M&Ms that emigrate from the Population cup. You'll also need a plate to catch the M&Ms you roll. Start a spreadsheet in Excel as shown in Figure 2.1.1 to record your population data.

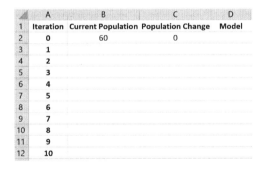

Figure 2.1.1: Setting up Excel to record population data.

1. For each iteration of emigration:

    (a) Remove 10 M&Ms from the Population cup and place them in the Roll cup.

    (b) Roll the 10 M&Ms cup in the Roll cup onto the plate.

    (c) M&Ms that land with the "m" side up are considered to have emigrated, so place them in the Emigrated cup and record the number of emigrants in your **Population Change** column of the spreadsheet.

    (d) M&Ms that land with "m" side down did not succeed in emigrating, so place them back in the Population cup.

    (e) Update your **Current Population** column based on the loss of M&Ms from the population.

2. Repeat the instructions in Step 1 to complete ten iterations.

3. The **Model** column is to be filled with an expected population after each iteration based on a mathematical model of our scenario. To create this model, consider the following.

   When we roll 10 M&Ms, while there is variation in how many land "m" side up, our expectation is that roughly how many will be "m" side up? That is, we expect what number to leave the population each iteration? Use this expected value to fill in the **Model** column with the predicted population for each iteration.

4. Give an equation that describes the data in the **Model** column.

5. In Excel, make a scatterplot of **Current Population** as a function of **Iteration**.

6. In Excel, start with your scatterplot in the previous question and add the **Model**, as a connected line, to the same plot. (This is a new skill; you may need to search online to find out how to make such a plot.) Give your scatterplot an appropriate title, label your axes carefully, and add your equation for the **Model** somewhere on the graph.

7. How does your model equation compare to the data?

8. Which of the following describes your population data with emigration?

   (a) Increasing at a constant rate

   (b) Decreasing at a constant rate

   (c) Increasing at an increasing rate

   (d) Increasing at a decreasing rate

   (e) Decreasing at an increasing rate

   (f) Decreasing at a decreasing rate

You have just created a dataset and modeled it with an equation. Congratulations! You have made your first mathematical model. You can model emigration for the Mint, Green, or Purple populations using the same process.

If you've completed an emigration simulation, you can review the immigration simulation next, or jump ahead to Part 3 on page 23.

Simulating Immigration

Simulating immigration works in much the same way as simulating emigration, except that we roll M&Ms to see how many people enter the population.

We will do the Yellow group example and simulate immigration data where the starting population is 4 people, and 6 people try to immigrate in each iteration. Start with three cups: one cup marked "Population" that contains the Yellow group starting population of 4 M&Ms; one cup marked "Roll" that you will use to roll 6 M&Ms at a time; and one cup marked "Immigrating" to hold the M&Ms representing those who potentially want to immigrate into the Population. You'll also need a plate to catch the M&Ms you roll.

Start a spreadsheet in Excel as shown in Figure 2.1.2 to record your population data.

	A	B	C	D
1	Iteration	Current Population	Population Change	Model
2	0	4	0	
3	1			
4	2			
5	3			
6	4			
7	5			
8	6			
9	7			
10	8			
11	9			
12	10			

Figure 2.1.2: Setting up Excel to record population data.

9. For each iteration of immigration:

   (a) Remove 6 M&Ms from the Immigrating cup and place them in the Roll cup.

   (b) Roll the 6 M&Ms in the Roll cup onto the plate.

   (c) M&Ms that land with the "m" side up are considered to have immigrated, so add them to the Population cup and record the number of immigrants in your **Population Change** column of the spreadsheet.

   (d) M&Ms that land with "m" side down did not succeed in immigrating. Use these and other M&Ms from the Immigrating cup to refill the Roll cup with 6 M&Ms.

   (e) Update your **Current Population** column based on the increase of M&Ms to the population.

10. Repeat the instructions in Step 9 for ten iterations.

11. The **Model** column is to be filled with an expected population after each iteration based on a mathematical model of our scenario. To create this model, consider the following.

    When we roll 6 M&Ms, while there is variation in how many land "m" side up, our expectation is that roughly how many will be "m" side up? That is, we expect what number to enter the population each iteration? Use this expected value to fill in the **Model** column with the predicted population for each iteration.

12. Give an equation that describes the data in the **Model** column.

13. In Excel, make a scatterplot of **Current Population** as a function of **Iteration**.

14. In Excel, start with your scatterplot in the previous question and add the **Model**, as a connected line, to the same plot. Give your scatterplot an appropriate title, label your axes carefully, and add your equation for the **Model** somewhere on the graph.

15. How does your model equation compare to the data?

16. Which of the following describes your population data with immigration?

   (a) Increasing at a constant rate

   (b) Decreasing at a constant rate

   (c) Increasing at an increasing rate

   (d) Increasing at a decreasing rate

   (e) Decreasing at an increasing rate

   (f) Decreasing at a decreasing rate

You can model immigration for the Blue, Red, and Pink populations using the same process.

Part 3: Making a Model Using a Trendline

The emigration and immigration models we developed based on the Orange and Yellow groups are called *first principle models* because they are based on the underlying principles that we expect 5 emigrants or 3 immigrants each iteration, and we knew the starting populations. It is often the case that we do not know the underlying principles behind a data set, so we cannot develop a first principles model. Instead, we must develop an *empirical model*, one that is based solely on the given data. One type of empirical model is a *trendline*, which is a function that fits the dataset well. In Excel, you can consider different trendline options and decide which one looks best. Let's practice doing this.

17. Open a new Excel tab, name it "Linear Trendline," and copy the **Iterations** and **Current Population** columns from the experiment into this new tab.

    Make a scatter plot of this data, then add a trendline. Make your trendline a Linear trendline, and choose to display the trendline's equation and R^2 value. (This is a new skill. If you are having trouble, try using the internet to search for "how to add a trendline in Excel.")

18. (a) What is the equation of the trendline for your data? It should look something like $y = mx + b$.

    (b) What do the variables x and y mean in the equation, and what are their units?

    (c) In your equation, what is the numerical value of m? What is the numerical value of b? What are their units?

19. What do the coefficients m and b tell us about the shape and/or position of the trendline?

20. What can the coefficients m and b tell us about the M&M population?

21. Using the equation of the trendline as a mathematical model for the M&M population, how many M&Ms do you predict there would be after 15 iterations?

22. Does your trendline go through each of your data points?

23. What is the R^2 value of your trendline?

24. When determining the "goodness of fit" of a trendlines, we often look at the R^2 value, which is a number that ranges from 0 to 1. Do an internet search to find the definition of R^2. Explain it in your own words.

25. Using what you learned about R^2, how good of a fit is your trendline for your data?

Assumptions

The emigration and immigration experiments have some *assumptions* built in. For example, we assume that each M&M has a 50% chance of landing "m"-side up and 50% chance of landing "m"-side down. Also, while it is possible that an M&M could land precariously balanced on its thin edge, it is quite unlikely, so we assume each M&M will land either "m"-side up or "m"-side down.

26. What assumption do we inherently make about how the color of each M&M affects its chances of landing "m" side up?

Since these assumptions are inherent to the experiment, and since our first principles model is based on the experiment, these assumptions are also inherent in the model. Making assumptions is a necessary part of the mathematical modeling process. Sometimes we need to make assumptions to simplify the problem so a model can be developed.

One should always take time to consider the assumptions one makes when developing any model, and let others know what these assumptions are. Sometimes these assumptions are wrong, and false assumptions can lead to inaccurate models and incorrect conclusions. Sometimes the assumptions we make are fine, yet others may look at our models and use them to create more complex, better models by replacing some of our assumptions with other information.

Review and Reflect

Take a moment to think back on this section. What were the main ideas? What did you find most interesting?

-

-

-

-

-

Linear Trendline Summary

- A *first principles model* is a mathematical model that is based on knowledge about how a data set is generated. It describes expected behavior, not accounting for randomness or other factors.

  - In the emigration simulation, let b represent the initial population and let m be *half* the number of M&Ms rolled each iteration. The first principles model was $y = -mx + b$.

  - In the immigration simulation, let b represent the initial population and let m be *half* the number of M&Ms rolled each iteration. The first principles model was $y = mx + b$.

- An *empirical model* is one that is based on collected data, with little or no knowledge of underlying factors that developed the data.

- One type of empirical model is a *trendline*, a function whose graph fits a given data set well. Spreadsheet software can quickly determine trendlines of data sets.

- Linear equations have the form $y = mx + b$, and can be determined either as a first principles or empirical model.

  - In our M&M experiments, the units of x were "iterations" and the units for y were "number of M&Ms."

  - The coefficient m determines how quickly the line rises or falls. When m is a positive number, the model represents a quantity that is increasing (as in the case of immigration). When m is a negative number, the model represents a quantity that is decreasing (as in the case of emigration).

  - The units of m are "the units of y per the units of x." In the M&Ms experiment, the units of m in both the first-principles and empirical models were "number of M&Ms per iteration".

  - Lines change at a constant rate; the rate at which they change is m. That is, every time x increases by 1, y increases by m.

  - The coefficient b determines the value of the model when $x = 0$. It has the same units as y. In our M&M experiment, it is/predicts the initial M&M population.

- Every model is based on certain *assumptions*. We should be mindful of, and open about, what assumptions we are making.

Exercises 2.1

Exercises 1 – 6 give basic practice understanding linear functions in multiple-choice form.

1. A country has a population of 20,000 and emigrants leave at a rate of 30 per month. What is the slope, m, of the equation for this model?

    (a) 10

    (b) 30

    (c) 20,000

    (d) -30

2. A country has a population of 85,000 people and emigrants leave at a rate of 7 per month. What is the slope of the equation for this model?

    (a) 85,000

    (b) $-85,000$

    (c) -7

    (d) 7

3. A town has 17 people moving into it each month (i.e., immigrants) and an initial population of 1500 people. Which of the following is the best model for this scenario?

    (a) $y = 1500x + 17$

    (b) $y = 17x - 1500$

    (c) $y = 17x + 1500$

    (d) $y = 1517x$

4. A country has 1100 immigrants entering each month and an initial population of 1,200,000 people. Which of the following is the best model for this scenario?

    (a) $y = 1,200,000x + 1100$

    (b) $y = 1100x - 1,200,000$

    (c) $y = 1100x + 1,200,000$

    (d) $y = 1,201,100x$

5. A population of 215 people has immigrants entering at a rate of 25 per month and emigrants leaving at a rate of 9 per month. Which of the following is the best model for this scenario?

    (a) $y = 25x + 215$

    (b) $y = -9x + 215$

    (c) $y = 34x + 215$

    (d) $y = 16x + 215$

6. An immigration/emigration model has the linear equation of $y = -4x + 110$. Choose the word/phrase that best finishes this sentence: The population is _____.

    (a) increasing

    (b) decreasing

    (c) staying the same

7. Suppose that Krasnovia, a small (fictitious) nation, recently reported a population of 146,241 people. Due to adverse political conditions in nearby nations, around 4000 people successfully immigrate to Krasnovia each year. If this trend were to continue year after year, what would Krasonvia?s population be:

    (a) After 1 year?
    (b) After 2 years?
    (c) After 10 years?
    (d) Create a first principles model of Krasnovia's population K after n years, and use this model to find the population 15 years after immigration began.

8. Suppose that Parumphia, a small (fictitious) nation, recently reported a population of 297,318 people. Due to low employment opportunities, approximately 800 people successfully emigrate from Parumphia each year. If this trend were to continue year after year, what would Parumphia's population be:

    (a) After 1 year?
    (b) After 2 years?
    (c) After 10 years?
    (d) Create a first principles model of Parumphia's population P after n years, and use this model to find the populations in 12 years.

9. In another M&M simulation, the collected data led to the trendline $y = 4.8x + 12$.

    (a) Is this a simulation of emigration or immigration?
    (b) What is the slope of this line and what does it represent numerically (with units)?
    (c) What is the y-intercept of this line and what does it represent numerically (with units)?
    (d) Knowing the trendline resulted from a simulation with M&Ms, how many M&Ms were likely rolled each turn? How many M&Ms did the simulation likely start with?

10. In an M&M trial, $y = 95.1 - 6.1x$ is the resulting linear trendline.

    (a) Is this a simulation of emigration or immigration?
    (b) What is the slope of this line and what does it represent numerically (with units)?
    (c) What is the y-intercept of this line and what does it represent numerically (with units)?
    (d) Knowing the trendline resulted from a simulation with M&Ms, how many M&Ms were likely rolled each turn? How many M&Ms did the simulation likely start with?

11. A company's revenues are modeled with the linear trendline $y = 4.2x + 37.3$, where y is millions of dollars of revenue and x is years since 2010.

    (a) What are the units of $m = 4.2$?
    (b) What was the company's revenue in 2010?

12. The height of a particular bald cyprus tree can be modeled with the linear trendline $y = 1.5x + 7.5$, where x is years since 2017 and y is the tree height, in feet.

    (a) What are the units of $m = 1.5$?
    (b) What was the tree's height when initially measured?

13. On a particular morning, the outside temperature is $45°F$ at 6:00 and is growing at a rate of $2°F$ per hour.

    (a) Give a linear model for the outside temperature. Specify the units of x and y.
    (b) Approximate the outside temperature at noon using your model.
    (c) Do you think this model will accurately predict the outside temperature at 8:00 that evening?

14. A company advertises a job paying $16 each hour.

    (a) Develop a linear model of the earnings y of someone who takes that job.

    (b) What is the y-intercept of this model? Explain why it is that number.

    (c) Many jobs pay "time-and-a-half" when an employee works more than 40 hours in a week. For this particular job, that means earning $24 each hour. Develop a linear model for the weekly earnings y of someone who has worked x hours more than 40 hours in a week.

15. The table gives the number of new homes sold in the U.S. since 2010.

Years since 2010	Number of new homes (thousands)
0	323
1	306
2	368
3	429
4	437
5	501
6	561
7	613
8	617
9	683

    (a) Make a scatterplot of the data, labeling the axes and giving the plot a title.

    (b) What is the equation of the linear trendline that fits this data, and what is its R^2-value? Include the line, equation and R^2-value on the graph.

    (c) What are the units of the m-value of the trendline? What does this number mean?

    (d) Use the trendline equation to approximate the number of new homes sold in 2022.

16. The table gives the number of votes cast in U.S. Presidential elections since 1980.

Years since 1980	Number of votes (millions)
0	79.4
4	92.0
8	90.7
12	84.0
16	86.6
20	101.5
24	121.1
28	129.4
32	128.8
36	128.8
40	155.5

    (a) Make a scatterplot of the data, labeling the axes and giving the plot a title.

    (b) What is the equation of the linear trendline that fits this data, and what is its R^2-value? Include the line, equation and R^2-value on the graph.

    (c) What are the units of the m-value of the trendline? What does this number mean?

    (d) Use the trendline equation to approximate the number of votes that will be cast in the 2024 election.

Exercises 17 – 18 describe an activity given in MA101_ExtraPractice.xlsx. **Each activity gives practice creating and using linear trendlines.**

17. The sheet MM_LinearImmigration_Problem gives data from another M&M activity. One can fit the data with a linear trendline and consider what that trendline tells us about the data.

18. The sheet MM_LinearEmigration_Problem gives data from another M&M activity. One can fit the data with a linear trendline and consider what that trendline tells us about the data.

2.2 Modeling with Exponential Trendlines

Group	Type of Change	Starting Population
Blue	Immigration	8
Yellow	Immigration	4
Red	Immigration	4
Pink	Immigration	8
Orange	Emigration	60
Mint	Emigration	45
Green	Emigration	60
Purple	Emigration	45

Part 1: Background

In the previous section we took a simplified look at immigration and emigration as factors of population change. However, in many populations, the most significant changes are due to the most natural of causes - birth and death. In this section we will perform simple simulations of birth and death with a population of M&M candies and use Excel to analyze our results.

Group Dynamics

As before, these M&M simulations can be explored alone, though it is beneficial to work in groups of 2 or 3. The instructions assume groups of three; individuals or pairs can easily modify the group assignments to fit.

Assign at least one of the following roles to each group member; everyone in the group should have at least one role.

- Leader: This cadet is responsible for reading aloud the handout and questions (including these roles that you are reading about now!) and generating discussion/helping the group articulate their plans to answer the questions. This cadet is also responsible for keeping the group on task and on track to finish within the time constraint.

- Spreadsheet Master: This cadet will be in charge of entering all the data into Excel; however, it should be stressed that the team as a whole determines the direction they are taking, so this cadet must be in constant communication with his/her team. Further, all cadets are responsible for understanding how to engage with the spreadsheet, so they must take the initiative to ask questions of the Spreadsheet Master if they don't understand how to manipulate the data/model. Multiple cadets may use computers, but the Spreadsheet Master is responsible for the official electronic record.

- Recorder/Reporter: This cadet will record the team's answers on the handout, including complete sentences to non-numerical answers. He/she will also be the spokesperson for the group. Multiple cadets make take notes or make written calculations, but the Recorder will be responsible for the official written record.

Part 2: Creating Data for Analysis

Setting Up

To get started:

- The Leader should start reading ahead to help the team understand what will be required for the experiment.

  You will be instructed as to whether to complete the Simulating Birth (on page 31) or Simulating Death (on page 32) activities. Go to those pages for instructions. Be sure to complete *only one* of these two activities.

- The Recorder/Reporter should collect a cup of M&Ms, two empty cups, and a paper plate. Mark one empty cup with a P (for "population"), and the other with an R (for "roll"). Mark the cup with the M&Ms with an X (for "extras").

- The Spreadsheet Master should prepare a spreadsheet for the activity by

    - opening a new spreadsheet (or use the spreadsheet used in the previous section),
    - naming a tab "Exponential Data", and
    - saving the spreadsheet. (If the spreadsheet is new, be sure to give it an appropriate name.)

Simulating Births

1. The Spreadsheet Master should create a table with three columns:

   - **Iterations** (starting at 0)
   - **Population Change** (starting at 0)
   - **Current Population** (starting at 4).

2. Remove the yellow M&Ms and eat them. We won't need them for the experiment.

3. Place 4 M&Ms in the P (population) cup.

4. Place all remaining M&Ms in the X (extras) cup.

5. Complete one iteration of birth as follows:

   (a) Toss the M&Ms in the P cup onto the plate.

   (b) M&Ms that land with the "M" side up are considered to be successful births, so add that many M&Ms from the X cup to the P cup and record this in the **Population Change** column.

   (c) All M&Ms that were rolled are placed back in the P cup.

   (d) Update the total number of M&Ms in the population cup after this iteration in the **Current Population** column.

6. Repeat the processes in Step 5 until ten iterations have been completed and record the necessary information in your spreadsheet. (If you ever reach a population greater or equal to 60, **STOP**. DO NOT include a population of 60 in your Excel data; your last recorded iteration should be the last one with a population under 60.

7. In Excel, make a scatterplot of **Iteration** vs. **Current Population**, providing appropriate labels and a title.

8. Determine which of the following describes the data.

   (a) Increasing at a constant rate

   (b) Decreasing at a constant rate

   (c) Increasing at an increasing rate

   (d) Increasing at a decreasing rate

   (e) Decreasing at an increasing rate

   (f) Decreasing at a decreasing rate

*** **Check in with your instructor before moving on to Part 3 on page 33.**

Simulating Deaths

1. The Spreadsheet Master should create a table with three columns:

    - **Iterations** (starting at 0)
    - **Population Change** (starting at 0)
    - **Current Population** (starting at 60)

2. Remove the yellow M&Ms and eat them. We won't need them for the experiment.

3. Place 60 M&Ms in the P (population) cup.

4. Place all remaining M&Ms in the X (extras) cup.

5. Complete one iteration of death as follows:

    (a) Toss all of the M&Ms in the P cup onto the plate.

    (b) M&Ms that land with the "M" side up are considered to have died, so place them in the X cup and record the number of these in the **Population Change** column.

    (c) M&Ms that land with the "M" side down have survived, so place them back in the P cup.

    (d) Update the total number of M&Ms in the P cup after this iteration in the **Current Population** column.

6. Repeat the processes in Step 5 until ten iterations have been completed and record the necessary information in your spreadsheet. However, if you ever reach a population of zero, **STOP**. DO NOT include a population of 0 in your Excel data; your last recorded iteration should be the last one with a population over 0.

7. In Excel, make a scatterplot of **Iteration** vs. **Current Population**, providing appropriate labels and a title.

8. Determine which of the following describes the data.

    (a) Increasing at a constant rate

    (b) Decreasing at a constant rate

    (c) Increasing at an increasing rate

    (d) Increasing at a decreasing rate

    (e) Decreasing at an increasing rate

    (f) Decreasing at a decreasing rate

*** **Check in with your instructor before moving on to Part 3 on the next page.**

Part 3: Making a Model Using a Trendline

In Section 2.1 we used first principles to develop a linear model of immigration/emigration of the form $y = mx + b$. We then used linear trendlines to form an empirical model of the immigration/emigration data we collected with M&Ms.

We have yet to make a first principles model of our birth/death scenario. We will first create an empirical model (an exponential trendline) of our M&M data, and use that to help us understand how to make a good first principles model.

9. Open a new spreadsheet tab and name the tab "Exponential Trendline". Copy your data from the experiment in Part 2 into this new sheet and reproduce the scatterplot of **Iteration** vs. **Current Population** previously created.

10. Using Excel's capabilities, add an exponential trendline on your plot, making sure to display the equation and R^2 value. Does your trendline go through each of your data points?

11. What is the R^2 value of your trendline and how good of a fit is your trendline for your data?

12. Record the equation for your trendline here. It should be in the form $y = Ae^{bx}$.

13. What does x represent? What is the numerical value of A, and what does it represent in this experiment? (Note: we will look at what b represents later.)

*** Check in with your instructor before moving on to the next questions.

Part 4: Making a Model using First Principles

The exponential trendlines given by Excel are equations of the form $y = Ae^{bx}$, where A is approximately the initial population. The manner in which the value b relates to the data is less obvious. In this section, we will develop a first principles model and explore the differences between our first principles model and the trendline model.

It is expected that one has only completed either the Birth activity or the Death activity. The activities are similar; here is a summary.

- In each iteration, all the M&Ms in the population are rolled, and the number that land M-side up are counted.

- In the Birth activity, that number of M&Ms are added into the population. In the Death activity, that number of M&Ms are removed from the population.

Remember that a first principles model is not based on any data – it is based on what we expect to happen. These activities shares an assumption of the immigration/emigration activities: each M&M has a 50% chance of landing M-side up.

We will walk through forming first principles models of both M&M birth and death. It is beneficial to read through both to fully understand exponential models.

A First Principles Model for M&M Birth

Our starting population is:

$$y_0 = A,$$

where y_0 represents the y-value at iteration 0.

After one iteration we have all of the population from before plus roughly 50% more since each candy has roughly a 50/50 shot at giving birth. Another way to say this is:

$$
\begin{aligned}
y_1 &= \text{starting population} + 1/2 \text{ of the starting population} \\
&= y_0 + 1/2 y_0 \\
&= y_0(1 + 0.5) \\
&= A(1 + 0.5) \qquad (\text{since } A = y_0) \\
&= A(1.5).
\end{aligned}
$$

We expect that after 1 iteration, the new population will be 1.5 times the starting population. (Another way of saying this is to say "The population will grow by 50%.")

Now consider the population after another iteration: we expect y_2 to be 1.5 times the size of y_1. That is,

$$
\begin{aligned}
y_2 &= y_1 \text{ population} + 1/2 \text{ of } y_1 \text{ population} \\
&= y_1 + 1/2 y_1 \\
&= y_1(1 + 0.5) \qquad (\text{now replace } y_1 \text{ with an equation from above}) \\
&= A(1 + 0.5)(1 + 0.5) \\
&= A(1 + 0.5)^2 \\
&= A(1.5)^2.
\end{aligned}
$$

Developing good mathematical models often depends on looking for patterns. So far, we have

$$y_1 = A(1.5)^1 \qquad \text{and} \qquad y_2 = A(1.5)^2.$$

(Notice the relationship between the subscripts and exponents.) It would be natural to wonder if the population in the next iteration would follow this pattern, and give

$$y_3 = A(1.5)^3.$$

Indeed, it does. Considering that y_3 is the y_2 population plus half the y_2 population, we have

$$y_3 = y_2 + 1/2 y_2 = y_2(1 + 0.5) = A(1 + 0.5)^3.$$

This pattern leads us to our first principles model for the population after x iterations:

$$y_x = y = A(1 + 0.5)^x.$$

Important: we can easily write $y = A(1.5)^x$, but it will be useful later to write the part inside the parentheses as "1 + something else," i.e., as $y = A(1 + r)^x$.

14. In the new form $y = A(1 + r)^x$, what does x represent, and what do the coefficients A and r tell us about the M&M population?

Consider the model $y = 10(1.25)^x$. We can rewrite this as $y = 10(1 + 0.25)^x$, and interpret this as modeling something with an initial value of 10 which is growing at a rate of 25%.

We now consider a first principles model based on our M&M Death activity. It is very similar to the Birth model we have just developed; note how in many places the "+" signs have been replaced with "−" signs.

A First Principles Model for M&M Death

Our starting population is:

$$y_0 = A,$$

where y_0 represents the y-value at iteration 0.

After one iteration we have all of the population from before minus roughly 50% less since each candy has roughly a 50/50 shot of dying. Another way to say this is:

$$
\begin{aligned}
y_1 &= \text{starting population} - 1/2 \text{ of the starting population} \\
&= y_0 - 1/2y_0 \\
&= y_0(1 - 0.5) \\
&= A(1 - 0.5) \qquad (\text{since } A = y_0) \\
&= A(0.5).
\end{aligned}
$$

We expect that after 1 iteration, the new population will be 0.5 times the starting population. (Another way of saying this is to say "The population will decay, or shrink, by 50%.")

Now consider the population after another iteration: we expect y_2 to be 0.5 times the size of y_1. That is,

$$
\begin{aligned}
y_2 &= y_1 \text{ population} - 1/2 \text{ of } y_1 \text{ population} \\
&= y_1 - 1/2y_1 \\
&= y_1(1 - 0.5) \qquad (\text{now replace } y_1 \text{ with an equation from above}) \\
&= A(1 - 0.5)(1 - 0.5) \\
&= A(1 - 0.5)^2 \\
&= A(0.5)^2.
\end{aligned}
$$

As before, developing good mathematical models often depends on looking for patterns. So far, we have

$$y_1 = A(0.5)^1 \qquad \text{and} \qquad y_2 = A(0.5)^2.$$

(Notice the relationship between the subscripts and exponents.) It would be natural to wonder if the population in the next iteration would follow this pattern, and give

$$y_3 = A(0.5)^3.$$

Indeed, it does. Considering that y_3 is the y_2 population minus half the y_2 population, we have

$$y_3 = y_2 - 1/2y_2 = y_2(1 - 0.5) = A(1 - 0.5)^3.$$

This pattern leads us to our first principles model for the population after x iterations:

$$y_x = A(1 - 0.5)^x.$$

Important: at this stage when developing the first principles model for Birth, we made a point of wanting to write the part inside the parentheses as "1 + something else," i.e., as $y = A(1+r)^x$. We actually want to do the same here; instead of writing $y = A(1 - 0.5)^x$, we write $y = A(1 + (-0.5))^x$.

15. We seem to prefer writing our exponential models in the form $y = A(1+r)^x$. If that is the case, what is the r-value in our M&M Death model of $y = A(1 + (-0.5))^x$?

16. Fill in the blanks with either the word "positive" or "negative":

    (a) In an exponential model of a growing population, the r-value will be _____.

    (b) In an exponential model of a shrinking population, the r-value will be _____.

First Principles Models Review

Consider the model $y = 10(1.25)^x$. We can rewrite this as $y = 10(1 + 0.25)^x$, and interpret this as modeling something with an initial value of 10 which is growing at a rate of 25%.

Consider the model $y = 20(0.9)^x$. We can rewrite this as $y = 20(1 + (-0.1))^x$, and interpret this as modeling something with an initial value of 20 which is decaying/shrinking at a rate of 10%.

17. Consider a different situation, where 6-sided dice are rolled, and only the dice that show a 1 "give birth."

    (a) What would the r-value be in this case?

    (b) If you started with 30 dice, what would the first principles model be?

18. Now consider a similar situation where again 6-sided dice are rolled, where only the dice that show a 1 or a 2 "die."

    (a) What would the r-value be in this case?

    (b) If you started with 80 dice, what would the first principles model be?

Connecting First Principle Models with Exponential Trendlines

Consider again the M&M's Birth scenario with $r = 0.5$. We will use this model to understand Excel's exponential trendline equations.

19. (a) Open a new spreadsheet tab and name the tab "First Principles Model". Make a two-column table where

    (b) the first column is **Iteration**, with values from 0 to 8, and

    (c) the second column, **Model Data**, has values using the first-principles model $y = 4(1 + 0.5)^x$, where x is the iteration number found in the first column.

        i. Use an equation to find the first value in this column. Write this equation so that it can be clicked-and-dragged down to compute all values in the column. Write your equation here for reference.

        ii. Your formula should return 13.5 for Iteration 3. If you did not get this value, re-think your formula and/or get additional help.

20. Create a scatterplot of your data with **Iteration** on the x-axis and **Model Data** on the y-axis. Then add an exponential trendline and show both the trendline and the R^2 value on the chart.

We should notice two interesting things.

21. First, the R^2 value should be 1. (If it is not, you should ask your instructor for help.)

    (a) Yes/No: We have seen R^2 values of 1 before.

    (b) Yes/No: We have seen trendlines go through each point exactly before.

    (c) Yes/No: This trendline goes through each point exactly.

    (d) Make a conjecture about when one gets a trendline with $R^2 = 1$.

22. The second thing you should also notice that instead of $y = 4(1 + 0.5)^x$, Excel gives the trendline in the form $y = 4e^{0.4055x}$. It turns out these are the same, though their equality is not obvious. To understand Excel's trendline, use an exponent rule:

$$y = 4e^{0.4055x} = 4\left(e^{0.4055}\right)^x.$$

To show that $y = 4e^{0.4055x}$ is the same as $y = 4(1 + 0.5)^x$, we just need to show that $e^{0.4055}$ is the same as $1 + 0.5$. Use Excel, with the command =exp(0.4055) to calculate $e^{0.4055}$. What do you get? Is it reasonably close to 1.5?

23. Suppose Excel is used to fit population data with an exponential trendline, whose equation is $y = 15.2e^{0.1398x}$.

    (a) What is the initial population?

    (b) What is the growth rate? (Use Excel to compute $e^{0.1398}$, then subtract 1.)

24. Suppose Excel is used to fit population data with an exponential trendline, whose equation is $y = 231.8e^{-0.2231}$.

    (a) What is the initial population?

    (b) What is the growth rate? (Use Excel to compute $e^{-0.2231}$, then subtract 1.)

25. Make a conjecture by circling either Increasing or Decreasing in each of the following sentences:

    (a) If a population is modeled by $y = Ae^{bx}$ and $b > 0$, then the population is Increasing/Decreasing.

    (b) If a population is modeled by $y = Ae^{bx}$ and $b < 0$, then the population is Increasing/Decreasing.

Assumptions

Our empirical models were built by rolling M&Ms and counting how many appeared "M"-side up, just as we did for the immigration/emigration activities in the previous section. As such, our assumptions for this activity are likely the same as they were before.

26. State one assumption made within the Birth and Death activities.

Review and Reflect

Take a moment to think back on this section. What were the main ideas? What did you find most interesting?

-

-

-

-

Summary

- We again saw *empirical* and *first principles* models.

  - An empirical model is based on collected/observed data. It does not rely on an understanding of the underlying factors that produced the data. The trendlines created by Excel are empirical models.

  - A first principles model is based on knowledge about how a data set is generated, often describing "ideal" behavior.

- Data that grows by a constant percentage over time is modeled well by exponential functions.

- When developing a first principles exponential model, it is natural to write it in the form $y = A(1 + r)^x$.

  - The coefficient A represents the value of the data when $x = 0$ (often this is the initial population).

  - The coefficient r represents the growth rate.

    * When $r > 0$, the model is growing/increasing.
    * When $r < 0$, the model is decaying/decreasing.

- An empirical exponential model is likely given in the form $y = Ae^{bx}$.

  - The coefficient A represents the value of the data when $x = 0$.

  - The coefficient b determines the growth rate.

    * Computing e^b gives the value of $1 + r$ (so computing $e^b - 1$ gives the growth rate).
    * When $b > 0$, the model is increasing; when $b < 0$, the model is decreasing.

Exercises 2.2

Exercises 1 – 4 give basic practice understanding exponential functions in multiple-choice form.

1. A bacterial colony has an initial population of 20,000 spores which die at a rate of 20% per week. What is the what is the A value of the exponential equation for this model?

    (a) 20

    (b) 0.20

    (c) 20000

    (d) 4,000

2. A bacterial colony has an initial population of 20,000 spores which die at a rate of 20% per week. What is the exponential equation for this model? (There may be multiple right answers.)

    (a) $y = 20000 \cdot 0.80^t$

    (b) $y = 20000 \cdot 1.20^t$

    (c) $y = 20000 \cdot 0.20^t$

    (d) $y = 20000 \cdot e^{-0.223144t}$

3. A bacterial colony has an initial population of 20,000 spores which die at a rate of 20% per week. During which week will the population first fall below 5,000?

    (a) during the 4th week.

    (b) during the 5th week.

    (c) during the 6th week.

    (d) during the 7th week.

4. The exponential equation for a population model has the form $y = 125e^{1.13t}$. Is the population increasing, decreasing or staying the same?

5. A population of 700 bats has a death rate of half the population per year due to White Nose Syndrome. If the population is modeled with an exponential model, what would the A value be?

    (a) 350

    (b) 700

    (c) 0.

    (d) -0.5

6. A birth/death model has the exponential equation $y = 100(0.8)^x$. The population is:

    (a) Increasing

    (b) Decreasing

    (c) Staying constant

7. A population of 120 experiences a death rate of one fourth of the population each year. Using the first principles approach, which of the following is the best model for this scenario?

    (a) $y = 120(0.75)^x$

    (b) $y = 120(-0.75)^x$

    (c) $y = 120(0.25)^x$

    (d) $y = 120(-0.25)^x$

8. A population of 150 experiences a birth rate of one fourth of the population each year. Using the first principles approach, which of the following is the best model for this scenario?

    (a) $y = 150(0.25)^x$

    (b) $y = 150(0.25)^x$

    (c) $y = 150(1.25)^x$

    (d) $y = 0.25(120)^x$

9. A birth/death model has the exponential equation $y = 110(1.2)^x$. How many people would you expect there to be after 3 years?

    (a) about 130 people

    (b) about 190 people

    (c) about 400 people

    (d) over 1,000,000 people

Exercises 10 – 11 describe an activity given in MA101_ExtraPractice.xlsx. **Each activity gives practice creating and using linear trendlines.**

10. The sheet MM_ExpBirth_Problem gives data from another M&M activity. One can fit the data with an exponential trendline and consider what that trendline tells us about the data.

11. The sheet MM_ExpDeath_Problem gives data from another M&M activity. One can fit the data with an exponential trendline and consider what that trendline tells us about the data.

Exercises 12 – 14 ask questions to help distinguish between linear and exponential models.

12. The number of visitors to park is increasing at a rate of 8 visitors per day, where the initial visitor population is 123. The visitor population is best modeled by a:

    (a) A linear model

    (b) An exponential model

    (c) Neither linear nor exponential is appropriate.

13. The number of visitors to park is decreasing by a third each month, where the initial visitor population is 123. The visitor population is best modeled by a:

    (a) A linear model

    (b) An exponential model

    (c) Neither linear nor exponential is appropriate.

14. Which population would be the largest in 5 years: Population A modeled by $y = 12x + 100$ or Population B modeled by $y = 100(1.12)^x$? Defend your answer.

2.3   Understanding Data Trends with Linear Trendlines

The previous sections introduced linear and exponential trendlines, essential tools when making empirical models of data. In this section, we explore further the proper use of trendlines:

- what they can/cannot tell us,

- how to format the data to more easily understand trendlines, and

- how to deal with data that isn't numerical.

    We will make use of the Excel worksheet `MtM_Unit1_CourseContent.xlsx`. The sheets with names starting with "DT_" contain a variety of data sets. The following case studies will use some of these data to explore important principles when using trendlines to model data.

Case Study 1: Population of Colonial Augusta County, VA

The size of a population is a basic fact necessary to good historical research. In Figure 2.3.1, some population data are given for Augusta County, VA, in the 30 years leading up to the Revolutionary War. The linear trendline seems to fit the data well.

Clearly, some data are missing. A historian, given this data set, may spend some time trying to find the missing data or at least understand why the data are gone. (For instance, we may find there was a courthouse fire in 1769 and some records were lost.)

The following questions help reveal what a linear trendline can tell us.

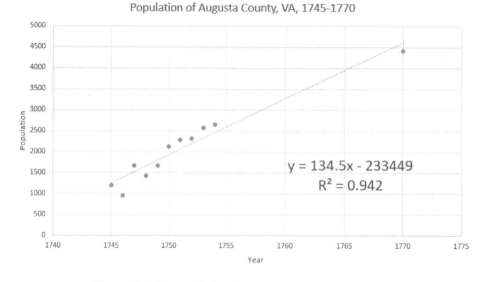

Figure 2.3.1: The population of Augusta County, VA, 1745–1770

1. The trendline implies that for the period between 1745 and 1770, the population of Augusta County grew by about how much each year?   134.5

2. Approximate the population of Augusta County in 1766 using the trendline in two ways:

    (a) By looking at the appropriate place on the graph.   3400 00

    (b) Using the equation of the trendline given on the graph.   4078

We can use trendlines to approximate data values in between known values. This process is called *interpolation*. We will also use trendlines to approximate values beyond known values; this process is called *extrapolation*.

3. Data for the missing years are not truly missing. The given data points were selected because, beginning in about 1754, something significant occurs in Colonial America that has a dramatic effect on the population, meaning your approximations above are likely far greater/less than the true value.

    Search online to find out what occurred in 1754. Would such an event tend to increase or decrease the population? Is your approximation above likely an over- or under-approximation?

    French & Indian War begin

4. Suppose a historian knows the years between 1763 and 1769 are relatively free of major population-affecting events and has only the following population data:

Year	1763	1764	1768	1769
Population	2562	2257	3478	3518

    Open a new Excel worksheet and label it "Linear Trendline".

    (a) Enter the four data points given. Use Excel to find a linear trendline to match these data and record its equation here.

    (b) Use your trendline to approximate the population of Augusta County in 1766 in two ways:
        i. By looking at the graph.   2760
        ii. Using the equation of your trendline.   2952

The actual population of Augusta County in 1766 is recorded to be 2873. You should have found that the trendline was off by 79 people, and it is natural to wonder "Is that a lot?" That is, is it ok to be off by 79?

The answer is "it depends." If you expect 100 people to attend a small concert and 79 fewer people show up, you would readily admit your expectations were *way off*. On the other hand, if concert planners expect 20,000 fans to attend an arena concert and 79 fewer people show up, no one would really notice.

One way to put this error into perspective is to consider it as a percentage of the actual population. This is called *relative error*, and it can be calculated as:

$$\text{relative error} = \left| \frac{\text{estimated value} - \text{actual value}}{\text{actual value}} \right|.$$

5. Calculate the relative error, given that the trendline estimated the population to be 2952 people. Is that relative error acceptable when doing historical research?

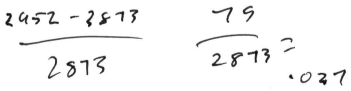

$$\frac{2452 - 2873}{2873} \qquad \frac{79}{2873} = .027$$

6. Population data for Augusta County is recorded in the DT_Augusta County tab of MtM_Unit1_CourseContent.xlsx

for the years 1745 – 1774. If one plots this data, one can see that the population steadily increases from 1758 until 1769.

(a) Fit the data from 1758 – 1769 with a linear trendline and record its equation here.

$$y = 78.719x - 136070$$

(b) What is the approximate rate of population growth during this time period?

~~78~~ 29 people per year

Case Study 2: Annual Visitation of Acadia National Park

Open the DT_Acadia NP sheet in MtM_Unit1_CourseContent.xlsx. It has the attendance records of Acadia National Park from 1980 until 2017.

7. Model the attendance data with a linear trendline.

   (a) Record the equation of your trendline here.

   (b) Does it seem to match the data well? Why/why not?

8. All the numbers in the data set are rather large, resulting in a trendline with large numbers. One very useful data analysis technique is to **shift** and/or **scale** the data so that the numbers are more manageable.

   (a) In the DT_Acadia NP tab, label column D as "Years Since 1980." In that column, let 0 represent 1980, 1 represent 1981, 7 represent 1987, and so on, giving a value for all the years shown in Column 1.

   There are at least two fast ways of creating this column: one way that uses a formula, and one way that does not. Record a formula that could be used in cell D2 to convert the year 1980 to 0.

   (b) Label column E as "Number of Visitors (in millions)". Let each value is this column be found by dividing the number of visitors in column B by 1 million. What equation could be used in cell E2 to divide the number of visitors in 1980 by a million?

   (c) Together, your two new columns create a new, but related, data set. Your first data point should be (0, 2.779666). (If this is *not* your first data point, work as a group to figure out what you did wrong and record your mistake here.)

   (d) One of your two new columns was created by *shifting* the data. One of your two new columns was created by *scaling* the data.
      i. Which column was shifted? Which was scaled?

      ii. What mathematical operations do you think one could use to *shift* data? What mathematical operations do you think one could use to *scale* data?

   (e) Find the trendline that fits your new data set. Record its equation here.

   (f) Compare this new trendline to the one found in Question #7. What "nice" qualities, if any, does each have?

9. What does the y-intercept of your new trendline represent? (Be careful about units.)

10. What does the slope of your new trendline represent? (Be careful about units.)

11. Would this trendline be useful in trying to predict the number of visitors to Acadia NP in 2018? Why/why not?

There is a significant drop in visitation from 1989 to 1990. While one could guess a number of reasons for a sudden decline in attendance, the truth is a factor that is often overlooked: the park changed the way it counted visitors between those years. This resulted in far fewer recorded visitors (and, ostensibly, far fewer *double-counted* visitors.)

12. A key principle in using data to perform analysis is *you don't have to use all the data*. Our goal for this question is to make a reasonable, educated approximation of the number of visitors to Acadia NP in 2018 based on a linear trendline.

   (a) What years of data would you like to use to make your approximation? Why did you choose these years?

   (b) Record the trendline calculated for your data.

   (c) Use the equation of your trendline to *extrapolate* and approximate the number of visitors Acadia NP will see in 2018.

13. Acadia National Park recorded 3,537,575 visitors in 2018. How does your approximation compare?

Case Study 3: Attendance at Cape Hatteras National Seashore

When dealing with data involving months of the year, it is common to let 1 represent January, 2 represent February, etc. When months of multiple years are used, January's fall on the numbers 1, 13, 25, etc. (i.e., spaced 12 apart, each 1 more than a multiple of 12). This is useful as one can look at a number and fairly quickly recognize what month of a year it represents.

14. In a listing of monthly data represented as described above, what month would $x = 33$ represent?

Starting in July 2015, the monthly attendance numbers were recorded for North Carolina's Cape Hatteras National Seashore.

Month	July	August	September	October	November	December
Attendance	388,146	353,743	298,610	168,031	107,526	59,943

15. Record this data in on a worksheet. Label the x-values with "Months of 2015", where you represent each month as discussed above. Label the y-values with "Thousands of Visitors" and **scale** the attendance numbers by dividing each by 1,000. This has the effect of making the numbers in your trendline smaller and easier to manage. (Your first attendance entry should be 388.146.) What is your fourth data point?

16. Model this data with a trendline and record its equation.

17. Is the clear downward attendance trend likely a cause for concern? Why/why not?

18. Would your trendline from above provide a reasonable prediction of February, 2016 attendance numbers? Why/why not?

19. Open the DT_Cape Hatteras NS worksheet of the MtM_Unit1_CourseContent.xlsx workbook. It contains the monthly attendance of Cape Hatteras NS from January, 2012, until June, 2016.

    How could this data be used to make a reasonable estimation of the July, 2016 attendance? Make a estimation: how many people attended this national seashore in July, 2016? (Be sure to both *explain* your methods and actually *make an estimation*.)

20. It is known that Cape Hatteras NS had 424, 324 visitors in July, 2016. Your approximation was *likely* an under-approximation. One point of this example is this: it is hard to make accurate predictions about human behavior just using trendlines, without additional knowledge of a particular industry. What other factors may be useful in making accurate predictions about park attendance? (You need not state *how* to use the information; just list factors you think may be useful.)

Case Study 4: Height/Weight Data

So far, we have used linear trendlines when the data looked roughly linear. Visually, our trendlines matched the data fairly well and that gave us confidence that our interpolation and/or extrapolation approximations were reasonable. Linear trendlines can also be used successfully when the data are clearly not linear.

Open the DT_HeightWeight tab of MtM_Unit1_CourseContent.xlsx. This is simulated height/weight data of 100 healthy adult males. (This is simulated data, so don't make any health decisions based on what you see here.) Create a scatter plot of the data.

21. Give a reason why a linear trendline does not seem appropriate when analyzing this data.

22. Give a reason why a linear trendline may be useful for analyzing this data.

23. Model the data with a linear trendline and record its equation here. What does the slope of the line indicate?

24. Suppose a healthy adult male is 5' 8" tall. How much do you expect him to weigh? What are some strengths/weaknesses of this approximation?

Review and Reflect

Take a moment to think back on this section. What were the main ideas? What did you find most interesting?

-
-
-
-

Summary

- Trendlines can be useful tools when filling in "missing parts of a story." We can *interpolate* with a trendline to approximate values between known data points, and we can *extrapolate* to approximate values beyond our data set.

- The slope of a linear trendline gives basic "rate of change" information. If the data set gives yearly rainfall in inches, and the slope of the line is 2, we could conclude that each year, about 2 more inches of rain fall than before.

- We do not have to use all of the available data to form a trendline and/or make an approximation. We can be selective.

- Shifting and scaling the data can be very useful. It creates trendlines with coefficients that are smaller, easier to understand and easier to manage.

- We should not model data without context.

    - Knowing that you are modeling inches per year can lead you to different conclusions than if you are modeling thousands of people per month.

    - One could conclude that Acadia NP became much less popular around 1990 based on the data. With context, we realize that the park service changed the way it counted visitors.

- All approximations based on trendlines are "educated guesses". They can provide a good estimate, and one should not expect them to be exactly right. Even when "wrong", they are more reliable than an uneducated guess.

Exercises 2.3

In Exercises 1 – 6, consider the scenario of recording the outdoor temperature in °F every hour, on the hour, starting on at noon on a Sunday. The questions ask about basic principles of creating models from data sets.

1. Is a model based on the collected temperature data a first principles model or an empirical model?

2. Suppose you've collected data through noon on Wednesday and created a model for your data. You want to approximate the temperature at 7:30 a.m. on Tuesday with your model. Is this an example of interpolation or extrapolation?

3. Suppose you've collected data through noon on Wednesday and created a model for your data. You want to approximate the temperature at 4:00 p.m. on Wednesday with your model. Is this an example of interpolation or extrapolation?

4. Suppose you've collected data through noon on Friday, and you want to create a model of the data so you can approximate the temperature on Friday at 2:00 p.m. When creating your model, you feel that the temperatures from Sunday through Thursday are not really relevant to the problem you are trying to solve, so you ignore them. Doing so is an example of what principle?

    (a) Interpolation

    (b) Extrapolation

    (c) The First Principle

    (d) You don't have to use all available data when creating a model.

    (e) Shifting/scaling

5. After collecting data through noon on Friday, you build a model and approximate the temperature on Friday at 4:00 p.m. to be 85.3 °F. At 4:00, the temperature is measured to be 86.1 °F. Of the following, which is the best conclusion that can be drawn?

    (a) While the model did not predict the exact temperature, it provided a fine approximation.

    (b) The model got it "wrong", predicting an incorrect temperature.

    (c) Next time we make a prediction, we should add 0.8 °F to the approximation and we'll get the correct temperature.

6. Suppose a portion of the data is modeled with a linear trendline. What are the units of the slope?

    (a) °F

    (b) °F per hour

    (c) °F per day

    (d) hours per °F.

7. The number of graduates from VMI is recorded each year, starting in 2003. The data begins with the following table.

Year	Number of Graduates
2003	212
2004	229
2005	249

    (a) If one were to build a model of the data, would it be helpful to shift/scale the x-values, the Year? If so, would one shift or scale, and by how much?

    (b) If one were to build a model of the data, would it be helpful to shift/scale the y-values, the Number of Graduates? If so, would one shift or scale, and by how much?

Exercises 8 – 10 refer to the following graph of the heights of 50 ragweed plants grown in soil with different pH values.

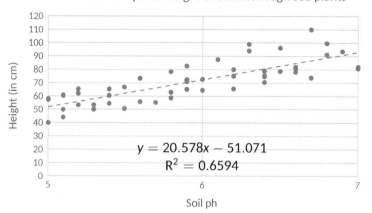

Affects of soil pH on height of common ragweed plants

$$y = 20.578x - 51.071$$
$$R^2 = 0.6594$$

8. What does the slope of the linear trendline tell us?

   (a) In soil with 0 pH, the height of a ragweed plant would be -51cm.

   (b) For every increase of 1 pH value (between 5 & 7), plants grow about 20.6cm taller.

   (c) About 65.9% of ragweed plants grow well in soil with pH values less than 7.

9. What does the R^2-value of 0.6594 tell us about the linear model?

   (a) The plants exhibit variation in their heights, and about 66% of that variation is explained by a linear relationship with the soil's pH value.

   (b) About 66% of the plants follow the linear model, with the other 34% not following the model.

   (c) The linear model is 66% accurate when predicting ragweed plant height based on soil pH.

10. Suppose ragweed is growing in soil with a known pH value of 5.5. What is our best approximation for the height of the fully grown plant?

Exercises 11 – 12 describe activities given in MA101_ExtraPractice.xlsx **on linear data sets.**

11. The sheet DT_LinearTL1_Problem gives the number of cadets who graduated from VMI from 2003 to 2018. One can construct a linear trendline for the data and predict the number who graduated in 2019.

12. The sheet DT_LinearTL2_Problem provides a large dataset of Dow Jones Industrial Average values. A linear trendline fits the data well and can be used to understand some of the behavior of the stock market.

2.4 Understanding Data Trends with Nonlinear Trendlines

Polynomial Models of Growth and Decay

Many quantities do not grow/decay with a constant rate of change nor a constant percent rate of change, and therefore are not well modeled by linear and exponential trendlines. For instance, consider the areas and volumes of squares and cubes, respectively, given their side length, as shown in the tables below.

Length	Area of Square		Length	Volume of Cube
1	1		1	1
2	4		2	8
3	9		3	27
4	16		4	64

One could not model either dataset well with a linear or exponential trendline. However, each can be modeled perfectly using a polynomial. The area of a square with side length x is simply x^2, which we often pronounce as "x-squared"; we can say that area grows *quadratically*. In a similar way, the volume of a cube with side length x is given by $x \cdot x \cdot x = x^3$; this relationship to a cube is why we pronounce "x^3" as "x-cubed", and we can say that volume grows "*cubically*".

These simple geometric relationships have physical implications. For instance, think about the size of the femur in an adult vs. a child. The adult leg bone is not just longer – it is also thicker. The femur of an adult that is twice as long as a child's will weigh more than twice as much. It will likely weigh between 4 (2^2) and 8 (2^3) times as much.

We can extend this idea to a whole person. A healthy three year old boy may have a height of 36″ and weight of 35lbs. Suppose he doubles his height by age 16; do we expect him to also double his weight? Of course not – a healthy 16 year old probably weighs much more than 70lbs. Our understanding of areas and volumes tells us that his weight should probably between 2^2 and 2^3 as much (and according to the CDC, a 16 year-old who is 6′ likely weighs about 170lbs).

Many quantities grow at rates not well described by linear or exponential functions, but rather by polynomials. This section explores some of these quantities and the use of nonlinear trendlines.

Deer Weight vs. Chest Girth

Open the DT_Deer sheet of the MtM_Unit1_CourseContent.xlsx workbook. It contains data relating the expected weight of a white-tailed deer given the girth of its chest. (Understanding this relationship helps biologists who study deer. It is not difficult to measure the girth of a sedated deer in the field, though it can be difficult to measure its weight.)

1. Plot the data and fit it with a polynomial trendline of degree 2, then 3, then 4. Record each equation here.

You might wonder, "which trendline is the 'right' one?" It is important to understand that when fitting a trendline to a set of data, there is often not a 'right' answer, though probably several clearly 'wrong' answers. The data do not seem linear, so we probably should not choose to model the data with a line.

A good rule of thumb is *use the simplest model that seems to fit the data well*. In practice, quadratic polynomials are often used when linear and exponential models are not appropriate; cubic polynomials are sometimes used and quartic polynomials are rarely, if ever, used. (We will see that our quartic polynomial has significant shortcomings that make other models better.)

2. Choose a model to estimate the weight of a deer with a chest girth of 50″. What model did you choose? Why?

3. Use the three polynomial trendlines you recorded above to estimate the weight of a deer with a chest girth of 32.5″. (Note: your quartic, or degree 4, trendline will likely give you an answer very far from something reasonable. We'll address this next.)

It is natural to wonder why the quartic approximation is so far from being reasonable, especially given the fact that the graph matches the data points so well.

The problem stems from the leading coefficient – the coefficient of the x^4 term. Excel shows it to be 0.0003, though it is really 0.000338274 and Excel rounded off. While it may seem that this should not make much of a difference, when you consider the size of $32.5^4 = 1,115,664.0625$, this difference actually matters. This is one of the shortcomings of high-degree polynomials, like quartics and quintics (which have degree 5), etc.

To address this problem, we could just use a simpler polynomial. For purposes of revisiting a previously–learned skill, we can also get past this shortcoming by recalling that we can shift/scale our data as learned in the previous section. In this particular case, shifting is probably all that is necessary. Instead of using girths between 20″ and 48″, we can shift all the data to range from 0 to 28, meaning 'inches beyond 20″.'

4. Shift your data as described and fit the new dataset with a quartic polynomial. Record the equation here, and estimate the weight of the deer with this model.

5. We used trendlines in problems #2 and #3 to approximate weights given a chest girth. Which approximation was an *interpolation*? Which was an *extrapolation*? What is the difference between the two?

Female Age vs. 50th Percentile Weight

The Centers for Disease Control releases data about the height and weight of girls age 2 to 18, categorizing the data according to **percentiles**. If a girl's height is **in the 40th percentile**, that means she is taller than about 40% of the girls her age (and hence shorter than 60% of the girls her age).

Open the DT_AgeWeight sheet of the MtM_Unit1_CourseContent.xlsx workbook. It contains the 50th percentile weight of girls by age.

6. Model the data with a polynomial of degree 2, 3 or 4. Record your model here. Why did you choose this model?

7. Use your model to approximate the 50th percentile weight of girls 10.5 years old.

8. The CDC data are specifically for girls with ages between 2 and 18. Suppose you want to use this data to estimate the 50th percentile weight for a 20 year old woman. Excel will graphically "Forecast" the trendline; by forecasting **2 units ahead**, one could visually see what your model predicts.

   Find the forecasting option and have it display your trendline through age 22. Describe the behavior of the trendline and whether or not it seems reasonable to use it to make a prediction past age 18.

   All three trendlines have shortcomings when extrapolating (or, forecasting) beyond the given dataset. We again recognize the importance of context when using trendlines. After a certain age, we expect people's weight to stablize and not grow/decline dramatically. Since all three trendlines show rapid change beyond age 20, each trendline is best used for interpolation and not extrapolation.

Constant Rate of Change vs. Constant Percent Rate of Change

Suppose a biologist needs to study mold spores. She starts (Day 0) with 10 spores in a petri dish. Each day after that the number of spores increases by 3.

9. Create a new tab in the Excel workbook and label it "Mold". Now, create two columns of data where column A lists the days 0 through 6 and column B lists the number of mold spores found in her petri dish.

   Fit a linear trendline to your data. What does your slope indicate? What does your y-intercept indicate?

   This is an example of population exhibiting a **constant rate of change**. After each time period the population grew by the same amount.

Now suppose the biologist starts with 10 mold spores on Day 0, and on each subsequent day, the number of spores doubles. (So there are 20, then 40, mold spores on Days 1 & 2, respectively.)

10. In your same worksheet, create two new columns of data. In the first column, list Days 0 through 6. In the second column, list the number of mold spores in her dish.

    Fit an exponential trendline to your data; it will have the form $y = Ae^{bx}$ for some values of A and b. What is your A-value and what does it represent? Note how the trend line fits the data exactly; record the equation here.

To understand the b-value of your trendline, recall the properties of exponents and our work studying the "birth and death of M&Ms". We were more interested in e^b than in just b itself.

11. Using a free cell in Excel, compute e^b and record it here. (It should be really close to 2.)

    Recall from our M&Ms Birth and Death work that if $e^b = 2$, we interpret that as $e^b = 2 = (1 + r)$ for some value of r, the **growth rate**. (In the M&Ms module, r was either the birth or death rate; in general, we can use "growth" to describe both, where birth has a positive growth rate and death has a negative growth rate.) So if $2 = (1 + r)$, then our growth rate r is 1. When a population is doubling every time period, it is growing by 100% each time period.

    This is key to understanding exponential growth. While linear functions have a constant rate of change, exponential functions have a **constant percent rate of change**.

12. Alter your spreadsheet by starting with 5 mold spores on Day 0, then each day tripling the number of spores for 6 days. What is your new trendline?

13. What is the A-value? Is this the value you expected?

14. Find the growth rate. Is this the value you expected?

We can also use growth factors to describe a shrinking population.

15. Alter your spreadsheet yet again. On Day 0 start with a population of 1024. Each day after that make the population half of what it previously was (so on Days 1 and 2, the population will be 512 and 256, respectively), for 6 days. What is the new trendline?

16. It can be easy to miss, but the exponent of your trendline should be negative. Making sure that it is, find the growth rate. Is this the value you expected?

Review and Reflect

Take a moment to think back on this section. What were the main ideas? What did you find most interesting?

-
-
-
-
-

Summary

- When data show a (near) constant rate of growth, modeling the data with a linear function is most appropriate.

- When data show a (near) constant percent rate of growth, modeling the data with an exponential function is most appropriate.

- When it isn't clear which type of model to use (exponential, quadratic, cubic, quartic, etc.) a good rule of thumb to use is to pick the simplest model that seems to fit well.

  - When a polynomial seems to be the best choice, quadratics are most common, followed by cubics.

  - Even though it is easy to make polynomial models with degree 4 or higher, these should be avoided.

- When using polynomials of high degree (degree 3 or more) with large x-values, be careful of round offs in the display of the trendline. These can give you inaccurate results when making approximations. Shifting the data values to have small x-values may help.

- Exponential models are very important.

  - A model such as $y = 5(4^x) = 5(1 + 3)^x$ represents something that quadruples each period (it grows by 300%).

  - A model such as $y = 5(1.1^x) = 5(1 + 0.1)^x$ represents something that grows by 10% each period.

  - A model such as $y = 5(0.25^x) = 5(1 - 0.75)^x$ represents something that loses 75% each period (that is, each period it is 1/4 of what it was before).

  - When given a model like $y = 5e^{0.405x}$, one can understand it by looking at the value of $e^{0.405} = 1.4993 \approx$ 1.5. That is, $y = 5e^{0.405x} \approx y = 5(1.5)^x = 5(1 + 0.5)^x$ represents something that grows by 50% each period.

- Interpolation is less susceptible to large mistakes than extrapolation. Be careful when extrapolating: models that fit the known data very well may behave in extreme ways beyond the data set.

- In practice, polynomials of degree 4 or more are rarely used. Using linear, quadratic and cubic functions are common. The next section will show us how we can use multiple functions to describe a data set which increases the value of linear, polynomial and exponential models.

Exercises 2.4

Exercises 1 – 7 provide basic practice of identifying which type of trendline to use to model data.

1. Which linear trendline would best represent this data set?

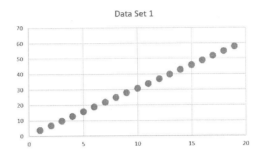

(a) $y = -3x + 0$

(b) $y = 3x + 0$

(c) $y = 0x - 3$

(d) $y = 0x + 3$

2. What R^2 value would you expect for a linear trendline of this data set?

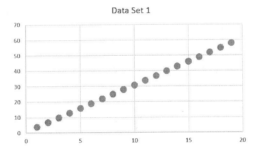

(a) A value close to 0, as the data looks exactly linear.

(b) A value close to 0.5, as the y-intercept appears to be close to 0.5.

(c) A value close to 1, as the data looks exactly linear.

(d) A value close to 3, as the slope of the line seems to be about 3.

3. What type of trendline would be best to model this data set?

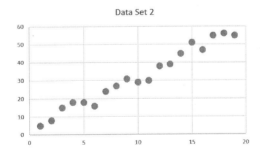

(a) Linear

(b) Quadratic (order/degree 2)

(c) Cubic (order/degree 3)

(d) Quartic (order/degree 4)

(e) Exponential

4. What type of trendline would be best to model this data set?

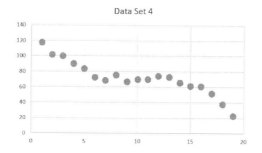

Data Set 4

    (a) Linear

    (b) Quadratic (order/degree 2)

    (c) Cubic (order/degree 3)

    (d) Quartic (order/degree 4)

    (e) Exponential

5. What type of trendline would be best to model this data set?

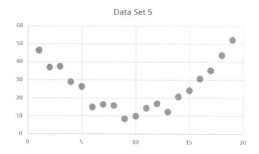

Data Set 5

    (a) Linear

    (b) Quadratic (order/degree 2)

    (c) Cubic (order/degree 3)

    (d) Quartic (order/degree 4)

    (e) Exponential

6. This data set was modeled using different polynomials and the R^2 value for each model is given. Based on the data set which model would be the best model to project future trends? Defend your answer.

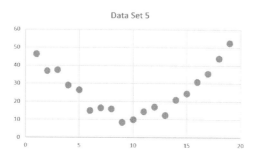

Data Set 5

    (a) Linear; $R^2 = 0.01$

    (b) Quadratic; $R^2 = 0.95$

    (c) Cubic; $R^2 = 0.97$

7. What R^2 value would you expect for a linear trendline of this data set?

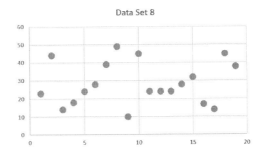

Data Set 8

(a) Close to 0

(b) Close to 0.5

(c) Close to 1

(d) One cannot say without complex calculations

Exercises 8 – 10 apply to the following table of the population in the USA

Year	USA Population
1950	158,804,395
1960	186,720,571
1970	209,513,341
1980	229,476,354
1990	252,120,309
2000	281,710,909
2010	309,011,475
2020	331,002,651

8. Create a scatter plot of the data, labeling the axes and giving the plot a title.

9. Find an exponential trendline for the data. What can you say about the A and b values? What else can you say about this model?

10. Shift the year data by subtracting 1950 from each year so that 1950 corresponds to zero. Scale the population data by dividing all of the numbers in the 2nd column by 1,000,000. Find the scatter plot and exponential trendline. Explain the new trendline, including why it is different than the previous trendline without shifting and scaling.

11. The sheet DT_NonLinearTL_Problem in MA101_ExtraPractice.xlsx gives the number of TikTok first-time installs from 2Q16 to 4Q19. The worksheet has one construct quadratic and exponential trendlines for the data and make future predictions of the number of first-time installs and cumulative downloads.

2.5   Analyzing Data using Trendlines

We have learned to model data with linear and nonlinear trendlines, and have used these models to better understand the behavior underlying the data. This section provides more practice using these skills.

The `MtM_Unit1_CourseContent.xlsx` workbook contains several worksheets of data in separate tabs that we will use in this section. The data are described on the next few pages, along with questions relating to that particular data set. You are to pick one (or more) of the data sets (your instructor may assign one to you). Open a new Excel workbook and copy your data set into its own tab. Be sure to save your file with an appropriate name and change the name of each tab to something descriptive. For each data set:

1. Plot your data and add an appropriate trendline with the corresponding R^2 value.

2. Explain why you chose this trendline.

3. Consider who would be interested in this particular data set and what they may use your trendline for.

4. Answer the questions associated with the data set.

Mile Runs

The worksheet DT_MileRuns contains the World Record Men's Mile-Run Times, starting with the record from 1913 until 1999, as recorded by the International Association of Athletics Federations.

1. Plot the data and add an appropriate trendline, displaying the equation and the corresponding R^2 value.

2. Why did you chose this trendline?

3. Who would be interested in this particular data set, and what may they use your trendline for?

4. (a) One can make an argument that interpolating doesn't really make sense for this data set. Why not?

   (b) One can give meaning to interpolation in the context of this data set. What is that meaning? Use your model to approximate the fastest mile run time in 1940.

   (c) Use your model to predict the fastest mile run in 2020. Does this approximation seem reasonable? Explain why/why not.

Netflix DVD Subscribers

The worksheet `DT_NetflixDVD` contains, among other information, the number of U.S. subscribers to Netflix's DVD service from 2012 to 2019.

1. Plot the DVD subscribers data by year and add an appropriate trendline, displaying the equation and the corresponding R^2 value.

2. Why did you chose this trendline?

3. Who would be interested in this particular data set, and what may they use your trendline for?

4. (a) Find the value given by your model for the x-value 2013.5. What does that x-value mean?

    (b) Use your model to predict the number of Netflix DVD subscribers in 2022. Does this approximation seem reasonable? Explain why/why not.

5. Model the data with an exponential function (if you have not already). What is the growth/decay rate predicted by the model?

Netflix Streaming Subscribers

The worksheet DT_NetflixStreamers contains the number of worldwide Netflix streaming customers, where time is broken down by quarters, starting with the 1st quarter of 2013.

1. Plot the streaming subscribers data by quarter and add an appropriate trendline, displaying the equation and the corresponding R^2 value. What does x represent in your model?

   # of quarters

2. Why did you chose this trendline?

   The closest to shape of plots

3. Who would be interested in this particular data set, and what may they use your trendline for?

   marketing

4. (a) The first column does not contain numerical values. If you haven't already done this as part of question #1, create a new column of x-values and explain what these x-values mean (i.e., explain how one could find the appropriate x-value for "Q1 2015", and given one of your x-values, how one could figure out the related quarter and year).

   -4 = 1 year

   (b) Model your data using your new set of x-values with the same type of trendline used in question #1. Record the new trendline here, along with it's R^2 value. How is it similar/different from your original trendline?

   There are fewer data points, and the r^2 is closer to 0

5. Netflix's subscriber growth slowed at the end of 2020. Using all the data to predict future subscriber counts would likely be inaccurate. We want to predict the number of subscribers at Q4 2022.

   (a) Select only some of your data to create a model with which you'll predict subscriber counts in Q4 2022. What data did you select? ~~228~~ *219.625   The last 3 quarters*

   (b) Model that data with an appropriate trendline. What model did you choose? What does your model predict the subscriber count in Q4 2022 to be?

Netflix Revenue

The worksheet DT_NetflixRevenue contains Netflix's annual revenue from 2002 to 2021, given in millions of dollars.

1. Plot the revenue data and add an appropriate trendline, displaying the equation and the corresponding R^2 value. What does x represent in your model?

2. Why did you chose this trendline?

3. Who would be interested in this particular data set, and what may they use your trendline for?

4. Use your model to approximate Netflix's annual revenue for the year 2022. Your answer will be in the units of the data, "millions of dollars." Convert your answer to more understandable units.

5. An exponential model fits the data well. If not done already, fit the data with an exponential model. From the model, compute e^b and give the annual growth rate of Netflix's revenue.

Smartphones

The worksheet DT_Smartphones gives the global smartphone shipments, per year, from 2009 to 2017 in millions of units.

1. Plot the smartphone shipment data and add an appropriate trendline, displaying the equation and the corresponding R^2 value. What does x represent in your model?

2. Who would be interested in this particular data set, and what may they use your trendline for?

3. The number of smartphone shipments decreased from 2016 to 2017. Suppose you are living in early 2018, looking at this set of data. Without additional knowledge about the smartphone industry, it is impossible to know if the 2017 data point is an outlier or is indicative of a changing trend. (The new trend could be continued decrease, or it could be maintaining a relatively constant level.)

   Knowing that smartphones remain very popular, why could smartphone shipments see a decline?

4. Fit only the data from 2009 to 2015 with a linear trendline. What does the slope of that trendline tell us?

Tesla

The worksheet DT_Tesla gives the number of Tesla vehicles delivered each quarter, in thousands of cars, from the first quarter of 2016 through the fourth quarter of 2020.

1. Plot the Tesla data *per year*, not per quarter, and add an appropriate trendline, displaying the equation and the corresponding R^2 value. What does x represent in your model?

2. Why did you chose this trendline?

3. Who would be interested in this particular data set, and what may they use your trendline for?

4. Remove the first data point (the total Teslas delivered in 2016) and plot the remaining yearly data. What type of model is the clear "best" that fits this data? What does its equation tell us about the number of Teslas delivered per year?

5. Use the model developed in Question #4 to predict the number of Teslas delivered in 2022.

Assignment: Model Your Own Data

Find a data set from anywhere on the internet related to a topic of your own choosing. Your data set must contain at least 5 data points, and must be of the type where fitting a trendline makes sense. (For instance, the data set of "the most popular baby girl names each year" cannot be fitted with a trendline.) Copy that data set into a spreadsheet, and make sure to record the web address somewhere on your spreadsheet for reference.

Answer the following questions in the form of a professional memo to someone who would be interested in your data set and analysis. In your memo, you will include the following:

1. To, From, and Regarding information. Here you must identify the appropriate stakeholder to which the memo is addressed. (I.e., think about your data and a professional would be interested in those data. Write a memo to that professional, addressing things he/she would care about.) You can look online for guidance about how a memo can/should be written (which you should cite in your Help Received statement).

2. A professional looking plot of your data from Excel that includes an appropriate trendline. Make sure to include the data itself in a 2-column table.

3. An explanation about why your model/trendline is appropriate for your data.

4. A forecast of your data 5 units beyond your data range. Include a discussion of what this forecast means and if it is reasonable.

5. Pick a value within the range of the first column of your data (it could be an existing point) and use the trendline to interpolate the resulting value. Explain why your stakeholder may be interested in knowing your approximation.

6. Include a discussion about any point(s) of special interest in your data set. This may include outliers, missing data, or any other unique characteristics of your data. If you wish to include further analyses (for instance, by removing an outlier and re-running your forecast), this would strengthen your case to the stakeholder.

2.6   Corn Syrup – Modeling With Multiple Trendlines

Background and Goal

In 1957 the process for the production of high fructose corn syrup (HFCS) was introduced in the United States. There are currently three kinds of HFCS's: HFCS-42 is made of 42% fructose, HFCS-55 is 55% fructose, and HFCS-90 is 90% fructose. HFCS-55 is the most commonly used, and it made its major appearance in sodas and other foods in the mid to late 1970's. The use of HFCS in the U.S. grew until sometime after the turn of the 21st century, when reports on adverse health affects of HFCS consumption became widespread.

   We will create a model for the consumption of HFCS with respect to the year. The level of HFCS consumption will be measured by the average daily number of HFCS calories consumed per person. The challenge of making this model is that the data shows different trends during different periods of time.

Part 1: Collecting and Understanding the Data

The United States Department of Agriculture (USDA) publishes reliable data for the U.S. consumption of HFCS. This data has been placed in the sheet CS_Table 52 of the workbook MtM_Unit1_CourseContent.xlsx. (One can find the same data via an online search with the terms *table 52 corn syrup*, which should bring up links related to the USDA Economic Research Service (ERS) Yearbook Tables; Table 52 gives per capita calories consumed daily by calendar year.)

1. What was the average daily caloric consumption of HFCS per person in 1970? What was it in 1980? (Remember to include units.)

2. How many calories of HFCS did the average person consume for the entire year in 1970? In 1980?

3. Soft drinks are often sweetened with HFCS. Assume that in one can of soda 99 out of the 130 calories are from HFCS. Using your answers from the previous question, how many cans of soda would one person have to drink in one year to match the caloric intake of HFCS in 1970? In 1980?

Part 2: Building a Model with One Function

Copy/paste the "Year" and "Calories consumed daily" columns into a new spreadsheet. Plot the data with **years since 1970** on the x-axis. (Note: this will require you to use your shifting skills from Data Trends.) It is clear that a linear or exponential trendline will not fit the data well.

   Fit the data with a polynomial trendline, starting with a quadratic and going up to order (or, degree) 6. One may notice that the quadratic model is not terrible, though the higher the order, the better the fit. After looking at these polynomial trendlines, have Excel display the equation and R^2 value of the 6th degree polynomial.

4. How well does this trendline seem to match the data? Does it seem to model well the overall trend of HFCS consumption? What is the R^2 value?

5. Are the coefficients of this polynomial easy to understand? Explain your answer.

6. Use the trendline to **visually** predict the HFCS consumption in 2025 (do not use the trendline equation). To do so, *forecast* the trendline ahead enough years so that $x = 2025$ is covered. (You may need to search online for *trendline forecast* to see how to do this.)

   Approximately how many daily calories from HFCS does this trendline predict?

7. Which of the following two statements you think is most accurate:

   (a) "Modeling all the data with a 6th degree polynomial may not yield useful short term predictions of HFCS consumption."

   (b) "Because the trendline is a polynomial with a high degree, it detects subtle trends in the data that indicate dramatically increasing HFCS consumption in the near future."

Part 3: Building a Model with Many Linear Functions

One can create a model of the consumption of HFCS that fits each data point *exactly* by connecting adjacent data points with a line. We now examine some of the advantages and disadvantages of this modeling strategy.

8. Create a scatter plot of all the data, but choose to make your scatter plot of the type where each data point is connected by a line. (You can do this by either creating a new plot, or you can select your old plot and choose to "change the plot type.")

   Does the resulting lines seem to visually match the data well?

9. Each line segment represents a new trendline as part of the overall model of the data. How many individual trendlines are used in your model? Does this seem like a manageable amount?

10. Use your plot to visually predict the level of HFCS consumption in 2020. How many data points did you use to make this prediction?

11. State which of the following two statements you think is most accurate:

    (a) "Since all known data is modeled exactly, modeling all the data with numerous linear trendlines can produce reliable predictions of HFCS consumption."

    (b) "Since each trendline only relies on two data points, the current modeling method does not capture general trends and may produce unreliable HFCS consumption predictions."

Part 4: A Compromise – The Piecewise Model

The previous parts were designed to illustrate that:

- often a set of data cannot be modeled well with just one equation, and

- there is such a thing as "too many trendlines."

12. Briefly describe why one may not want to use a single high order polynomial to describe a set of data.

13. Briefly describe why one may not want to use a large number of trendlines to describe a set of data.

14. Look at a plot of all the HFCS data (you may create a new plot or you may just look at a plot generated before). From 1970 until 1985, the consumption of HFCS seems to follow a particular trend that changes after 1985. Break the remaining years into to more intervals, where the consumption trend seems consistent on each interval.

1970   to   1985   ;

1985   to &underline;   ;

&underline;   to &underline;.

15. We will now make a plot of the data with a different trendline for each of the intervals listed above. This is creating a *piecewise model*; it is one model of the data, consisting of several distinct pieces.

    (a) Make a plot of the HFCS from your first interval of years (from 1970 to 1985). Model this data with a linear or quadratic trendline (pick the most appropriate) and include the equation of the trendline, with R^2 value, on the plot.

    (b) Add the data from the second range to your chart. An online search may again help; it may help to know that you will likely use the "Select Data" or "Select Range" option of your spreadsheet. Again pick an appropriate trendline (**linear** or **quadratic**) for this new data range, and display the equation of the trendline and its R^2 value on the plot.

    (c) Repeat the above step for the last data range. Format your plot so each trendline has a distinct color.

16. List the equations of the three trendlines from your plot.

17. Forecast with your third trendline to approximate the HFCS consumption in 2025.

Review and Reflect

Take a moment to think back on this section. What were the main ideas? What did you find most interesting?

-

-

-

-

-

Summary

- When a set of data exhibits multiple types of trends, two common, yet poor, choices for modeling the data are:

  - to choose one high degree polynomial to model all the data, or
  - to "connect the dots" with linear trendlines between each pair of data points.

- While a high-degree polynomial may fit the data well (with R^2 value near 1), it:

  - is usually not well suited for extrapolation (either growing or declining very rapidly), and
  - the coefficients of the model are often large and hard to use.

- While linear trendlines between each data point matches the data exactly,

  - extrapolation depends only on the last two data points, ignoring general trends, and
  - it is impractical to keep track of a large number of linear equations.

- A piecewise model of a set of data is one model that consists of two or more distinct pieces.

  - The pieces are chosen to fit data that show a common trend.
  - The basic principles of choosing a trendline learned from Data Trends apply to each piece (for instance, choose the simplest model that fits well).
  - The last x-value from one piece is the first x-value of the subsequent piece of the model. (E.g., in the corn syrup example, the year 1985 ended the first interval and began the second.)

Assignment: Modeling With a Piecewise Model

The consumption of high fructose corn syrup is only one example of how something in the real world can grow and/or decline in different ways during different periods of time, necessitating a piecewise model.

For this project, each group will either find their own data set or choose a data set from the list given below. Once this data set is chosen, each member of the group needs to submit their own report that considers each of the following. (Note: your report should read and flow well, not consisting of an enumerated list.)

- What narrative can this data set tell? What understanding can this data set provide? In short, determine why anyone would care about the data set you chose.

- Determining why someone would be interested in your data set goes hand-in-hand with determining who that someone is. Think about what audience cares about your particular data set and write to that audience.

- Your report should include a synopsis of the observed trends in the past, along with an explanation of those trends based on real-world factors.

- Model your data set with a piecewise function. Include the model somewhere in your report, using proper notation, along with a graph of the data and model. Your graph should contain all the "usual" things: titles, labels, trendlines and their equations, etc.

- Include a copy of the data you used in a well-formatted table.

- Describe the behavior you expect to see in the near future from the quantity you are modeling.

- What are the strengths and weaknesses of your model? How well did your trendlines fit the data? How confident are you in the predictions you made?

- Your report should have an introduction and a conclusion. Think about what information should be included first in the introduction and what should be included last in the conclusion. Remember that the introduction should include some conclusions from your analysis; let the reader know upfront what the data are illustrating.

Possible data sets:

- S & P Case Shiller U.S. National Home Price Index:

  https://www.statista.com/statistics/199360/case-shiller-national-home-price-index-for-the-us-since-2000/

- Population of Albania:

  http://data.worldbank.org/indicator/SP.POP.TOTL?locations=AL

- Refugee population of Turkey:

  http://data.worldbank.org/indicator/SM.POP.REFG?locations=TR&view=chart

$$f(x) = \begin{cases} x+1 & \text{if } x \neq 1 \\ 2x+3 & \text{if } x = 1 \end{cases}$$

Exercises 2.6

1. Consider the following graph of square miles of forest in Chile, by year.

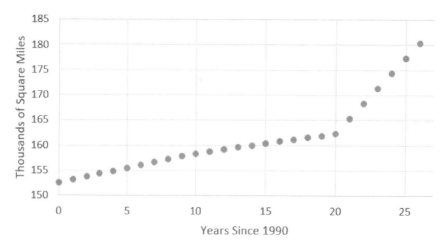

If modeling this data with two linear trendlines, which of the following is the best way to break up the data?

(a) Line 1: From 0 to 20 and Line 2: From 21 to 26

(b) Line 1: From 0 to 20 and Line 2: From 20 to 26

Exercises 2 – 4 use the following graph on U.S. construction spending on federal highway and street projects.

Note that y represents the value of the federal highway and street projects in millions of U.S. dollars and x represents the year.

2. Where would you break up the data in order to model it with three linear trendlines?
   First Trendline: from 2008 to _____.
   Second Trendline: from _____ to _____.
   Third Trendline: from _____ to 2018.

3. Where would you break up the data in order to model it with one linear trendline and one quadratic trendline?
   First Trendline: from 2008 to _____.
   Second Trendline: from _____ to 2018.

4. The coefficients for all linear and quadratic trendlines involving this data are large. Which of the following techniques would make the trendline equations easier to manage?

   (a) Scale the y axis by multiplying each value by 1,000,000.

   (b) Scale the y axis by dividing each value by 1,000,000.

   (c) Shift the x-axis by subtracting 2008 from each year.

Exercises 5 – 7 use the following graph, which depicts the price of Bitcoin in U.S. dollars.

5. Notice that the price of Bitcoin is missing for several months in 2018. Which x-value corresponds to June 2018?

   (a) $x = 18$

   (b) $x = 19$

   (c) $x = 20$

   (d) $x = 21$

6. Use the trendline model to approximate the price of Bitcoin in June 2018.

7. Notice that some of the coefficients in each of the trendlines in the figure above are very large. Looking back at the graph, which of the following techniques would make these equations easier to manage?

   (a) Scale the y-axis by multiplying each value by 1,000.

   (b) Scale the y-axis by dividing each value by 1,000.

   (c) Shift the x-axis by adding 2016 to each value.

   (d) Shift the x-axis by subtracting 2016 to each value.

8. Consider the following two figures depicting the number of satellites launched between 1957-2018:

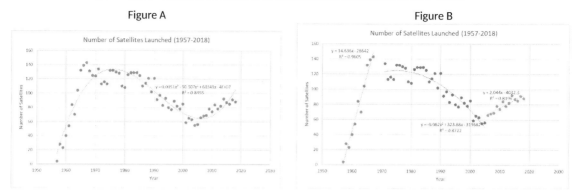

Figure A   Figure B

Which trendline model will best predict the number of satellites to be launched in 2020? Choose the best model and justification.

(a) Figure A - this trendline generally has a higher R^2 value, and thus is a better fit of the data set.

(b) Figure A - a third order polynomial fits the data better than 3 separate trendlines.

(c) Figure B - though the last "piece" of the model has a lower R^2 value, a linear trendline better captures the immediate behavior of the data near 2020.

(d) Figure B - this model contains a trendline with the highest R^2 value.

9. The worksheet CS_MultiTL_Problem in the workbook MA101_ExtraPractice.xlsx contains data about the total number of COVID-19 cases in the U.S. The data is best modeled with multiple trendlines. The activity in the worksheet seeks insight into the spread of COVID in the U.S. through the trendlines, and demonstrates why a single trendline isn't appropriate.

Chapter 3

Describing Large Data Sets

In the previous chapter we looked at describing a set of data with a trendline. Trendlines are not the appropriate descriptive tool for all sets of data, however.

Consider collecting the starting salary of all graduates from a particular college in 2021. That set of data could contain thousands of numbers. How would you describe that data to someone else? What would you want to know about that data so that you could "understand" it well? What would it mean to "graph the data"? And suppose you had such salary information from several colleges. How could you compare the starting salary data across schools?

Trendlines would not be an effective analysis tool for these data. Rather, one would likely be interested in the average, or *mean*, salary. But that is just a starting point. In this chapter we'll discuss ways of analyzing large data sets and effective ways of describing them, both graphically and numerically. (And along the way, we'll see why the *median* is likely a better tool to describe salaries than the mean.)

This chapter begins with a study of what it takes to make a good (and bad) graphic that is supposed to communicate information to others.

3.1   Communicating Data

Many people are familiar with the saying "A picture is worth a thousand words." And when it comes to describing sets of data, a well-constructed graphic can be very useful.

But producing well-constructed graphics is not trivial. Many well-intentioned people create graphics that can lead the reader to incorrect conclusions. (This often happens when one tries to make a "fancy" or "impressive" looking graphic, instead of something more "plain.") And worse yet, one can intentionally make a graphic that is "technically correct", but still misleads the audience to a desired interpretation.

For instance, consider the graphic of online bed bug reviews given in Figure 3.1.1. Before reading on, take a moment to understand what the graphic is supposed to communicate to you.

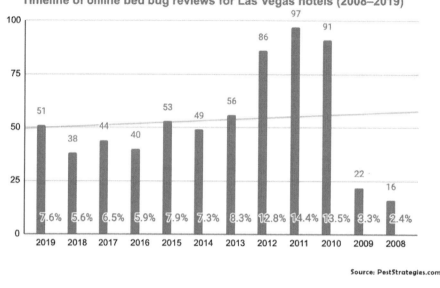

Figure 3.1.1: An example of a poorly constructed graphic.
(Accessed 7/10/2021 from https://www.peststrategies.com/exterminators/nevada/las-vegas/top-10-bed-bug-hotels-in-las-vegas-for-2021/#more-3041157.)

This particular graphic, while looking impressive, is fraught with bad design issues. Here's a partial list:

- While it is good that the graphic has a title, it is actually not very descriptive. It says it is a "timeline of reviews"; is it actually giving a timeline of the *number* of reviews?

- The *x*-axis is not labelled, but one can safely assume those numbers are years. However, the *y*-axis is not labelled. Do the numbers from 0 to 100 represent "numbers of reviews"? Since the numbers go to 100, one may think they represent percents.

- The years are listed in reverse order. That is confusing.

- One may assume that the blue line is a trendline. If it is, it is confusing at the years are backwards so it is actually showing a downward trend.

- There's a big jump in the blue bars from 2009 to 2010; the trend changes. The maker of this graphic didn't heed the advice of "trendlines don't have to use all the data."

- The red percentages across the bottom are given without any context.

This section presents a number of graphics that demonstrate a variety of shortcomings. Some are so poorly constructed that most readers won't even know what they are looking at; some may unintentionally lead the audience to an improper conclusion; some may intentionally mislead the reader. For each of the graphics shown, consider the following two questions:

- What is the message the picture is trying to convey?

- What are the shortcomings with the graph and its message?

As you consider each graphic, consider issues such as clarity of presentation, titles, axis labels, scaling, incorrect information, improper plots types, etc.

1. Trash

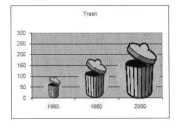

(a) What is the message the picture is trying to convey?

(b) What are the shortcomings with the graph and its message?

2. Happy Birthday!

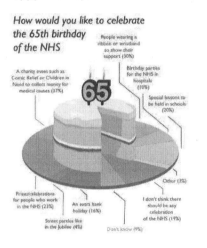

(a) What is the message the picture is trying to convey?

(b) What are the shortcomings with the graph and its message?

3. Scared of Zika?

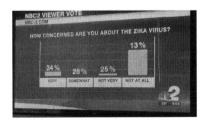

(a) What is the message the picture is trying to convey?

(b) What are the shortcomings with the graph and its message?

4. Nutrition

(a) What is the message the picture is trying to convey?

(b) What are the shortcomings with the graph and its message?

5. Gun deaths

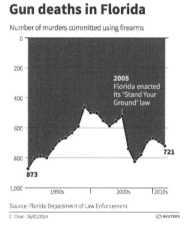

(a) What is the message the picture is trying to convey?

(b) What are the shortcomings with the graph and its message?

6. Junk Food

(a) What is the message the picture is trying to convey?

(b) What are the shortcomings with the graph and its message?

7. Commuters

(a) What is the message the picture is trying to convey?

(b) What are the shortcomings with the graph and its message?

8. Happiness

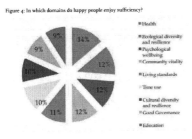

(a) What is the message the picture is trying to convey?

(b) What are the shortcomings with the graph and its message?

9. Home Value

(a) What is the message the picture is trying to convey?

(b) What are the shortcomings with the graph and its message?

10. U.K. Food Sources

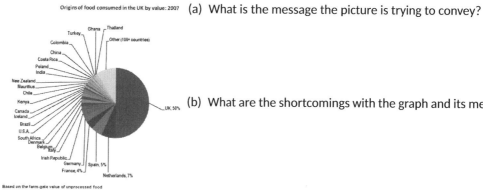

(a) What is the message the picture is trying to convey?

(b) What are the shortcomings with the graph and its message?

11. Education

(a) What is the message the picture is trying to convey?

(b) What are the shortcomings with the graph and its message?

12. Pitching decline

(a) What is the message the picture is trying to convey?

(b) What are the shortcomings with the graph and its message?

13. Jobs and Insurance

(a) What is the message the picture is trying to convey?

(b) What are the shortcomings with the graph and its message?

The previous three graphics illustrate an important principle: if a graph has a y-axis, then that y-axis scale should include 0. Without 0, small changes can be made to look very large. In the space below, sketch one of the graphics from # 11, 12 or 13, including 0 on the y-axis.

The rule "the y-axis should include 0" is not absolute, though. Consider the Uninsured Americans graph in #13. Suppose an economist knows that it is extremely rare for uninsured rates to grow by 3 million people over the span of 2 years. The economist knows, from his expertise, that this type of growth is unusual and significant. He would likely want to create a graphic that indicates this importance, and a graph that includes 0 on the y-axis would actually *hide* that important growth.

This leads us to a fundamental principle of this section: graphics are to clearly communicate important ideas. In general, including a 0 on a y-axis is good, because it lets the numbers "speak for themselves" without introducing subconscious bias. However, there are times where an idea is more clearly communicated with a different y-axis scale.

As a *consumer* of graphical information – that is, as one who looks at graphics created by others – be mindful of this principle. If the graphic does not include 0, ask yourself "Why not?" Perhaps the creator was careless; perhaps the creator was intentionally trying to manipulate you; perhaps the creator was trying to make a fair, true point clear.

The next few graphics are intentionally "bad", created with the goal of illustrating common mistakes when creating informational graphics. For each, identify what point the creator was trying to make about good graphic-making principles.

14. Yes/No

What point is the creator trying to make with this graphic?

15. Death by Dihydrogen Monoxide

What point is the creator trying to make with this graphic?

16. Evil Nick Cage

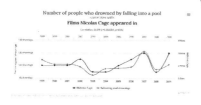

What point is the creator trying to make with this graphic?

Review and Reflect

Take a moment to think back on this section. What were the main ideas? What did you find most interesting?

-

-

-

-

-

Communicating Data Summary

When presenting data in a graph, here are some guidelines.

Do:

- Have a clear message. Present the data so that it's as easy as possible for the viewer to make sense of it.

- Include a title and label the axes.

- Use a legend when plotting more than one set of data on a single graph. Use different colors or line styles to differentiate the data sets.

- Use scales for the axes that

    - are easy to interpret,
    - include zero on the y-axis, and
    - tick off consistent amounts with no gaps.

- Make sure the graph reflects the data accurately.

- Choose an appropriate type of graph for the data. For example, we saw in the examples that a pie chart can be a reasonable or a poor choice depending on the data. Note that some people or companies strongly prefer bar charts to pie graphs.

You may, with care:

- Use two different vertical y-axes, with different scales for each one.

- *Not* include 0 on the y-axis to emphasize a fair, important change.

Do not:

- Represent amounts using differently sized images/icons (as in the fast-food example above).

- Use distracting color or 3D effects.

Assignment: Reports To Congress

Background:

Every year, some of the liveliest discussions on Capitol Hill surrounded the National Defense Authorization Act (NDAA), which, in short, gives the Department of Defense the ability to spend its budget. Each Congress imposes certain conditions on the Department of Defense, including certain reporting requirements to help Congress know that the money they allocated was put to good use. Starting in the 2015 NDAA, Congress has requested semiannual reports on "Ensuring Security and Stability in Afghanistan".

These reports are often put together quickly, and sometimes in the rush, these reports are not as polished as they should be. In this assignment, you will look at some actual reports that the Department of Defense submitted to Congress.

This assignment asks you to write a short report assessing the quality of some specific graphics in these reports, specifically the graphs designed to address Congress's mandate to include the number of effective enemy-initiated attacks.

Resources:

You can find the reports in at least one of the following ways.

- Download them using an online search similar to "department of defense 1225 *year*", where *year* is 2015, 2016, 2017 and 2018. (The number 1225 is important to include in the search, as it specifies what report we are looking for.)

- Download them using the links provided:

  - December 2015:
    ```
    https://dod.defense.gov/Portals/1/Documents/pubs/1225_Report_Dec_2015_-_Final_20151210.pdf
    ```
  - December 2016:
    ```
    https://dod.defense.gov/Portals/1/Documents/pubs/Afghanistan-1225-Report-December-2016.pdf
    ```
  - December 2017:
    ```
    https://media.defense.gov/2017/Dec/15/2001856979/-1/-1/1/1225-REPORT-DEC-2017-FINAL-UNCLASS-BASE.PDF
    ```
  - December 2018:
    ```
    https://media.defense.gov/2018/Dec/20/2002075158/-1/-1/1/1225-REPORT-DECEMBER-2018.PDF
    ```

- They may be provided by your instructor.

What you need to do:

1. Download the reports from December 2015 through December 2018, as indicated above.

2. Search each report for a graphic on the number of *effective enemy-initiated attacks*. (Use the Search capability of your pdf viewer to do this; DO NOT read the whole report!)

3. Write a short report assessing the quality of these graphics. In your report, insert a copy of each graphic, ordered from "worst" to "best". Be sure that you clearly label each of the four graphics so the reader knows which report they came from.

4. Justify your ordering of the graphics. What are the shortcomings of each, and what do the "good" graphics do well?

5. Good communication skills go beyond making good graphics; saving reports *with good filenames* is also important. Each of the urls for the reports above contain the report's filename. What is good/bad about the way these reports are named?

Exercises 3.1

Exercises 1 – 2 refer to graphic in Figure 3.1.2.

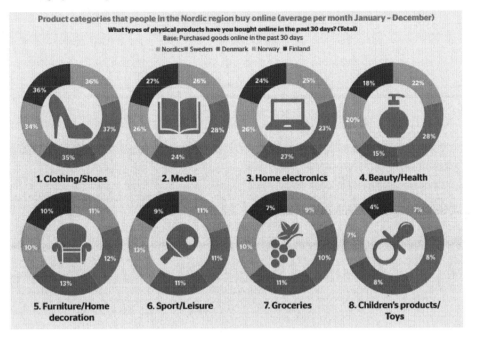

Figure 3.1.2

1. Which of the following best describes the message of this graph?

   (a) People in the Nordic region buy too many clothes and shoes online.

   (b) The general online shopping habits of people in the Nordic region.

   (c) The percentages of online purchases in each of the 8 listed categories by country in the Nordic region.

   (d) People in Nordic countries prioritize home electronics over groceries.

2. What is the most significant shortcoming of the graphic?

   (a) The title and graphs are not well aligned, as the title refers to averages and totals while the graphs use percentages.

   (b) The percentages of each section do not add up to 100%.

   (c) The color choices are confusing - it is difficult to tell sections of each pie chart apart.

   (d) The figure has no significant shortcomings.

Exercises 3 – 5 refer to the graphic in Figure 3.1.3.

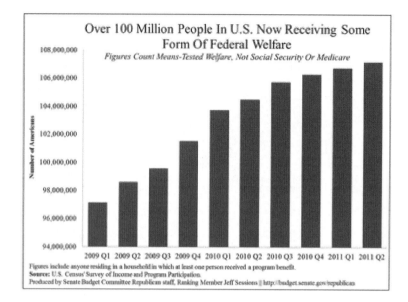

Figure 3.1.3

3. Which of the following most likely describes the intended message of this graph?

   (a) There was no significant change in the number of Americans on welfare between 2009-2011.

   (b) The number of Americans on welfare increased between 2009-2011.

   (c) The number of Americans on welfare greatly increased between 2009-2011.

   (d) None of the above.

4. What is the most significant shortcoming of the graphic?

   (a) The graph uses quarters instead of years on the *x*-axis.

   (b) The graph has scaling issues because the *y*-axis does not begin at zero.

   (c) The numbers for each bar add up to more than 100%.

   (d) The units of the *y*-axis should be "millions of Americans" so the numbers would be 94, 96, etc., which are easier to read.

5. Who among the following would likely use this graph as part of their job?

   (a) A conservative lobbying group trying to emphasize an increase in the number of Americans on welfare during Barack Obama's first term as president.

   (b) A liberal lobbying group trying to emphasize the strength of the economy during Barack Obama's first term as president.

Exercises 6 – 7 refer to the graphic in Figure 3.1.4.

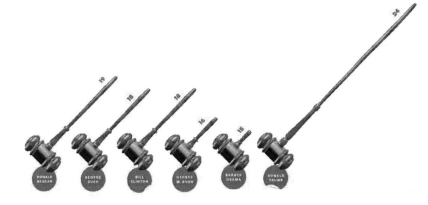

PRESIDENT TRUMP'S JOB APPROVAL
AMONG REPUBLICANS

| APPROVE | 88% |
| DISAPPROVE | 9% |

NBC NEWS/WALL STREET JOURNAL POLL
JULY 15-18
MOE +/- 3.27 PTS

DEVELOPING

Figure 3.1.4

6. Which of the following best describes the message of this graph?

  (a) Only a few Democrats disapprove of Donald Trump's presidency.

  (b) An overwhelming majority of people approve of Donald Trump's presidency.

  (c) An overwhelming majority of Republicans approve of Donald Trump's presidency.

  (d) There is a small percentage of people who neither approve nor disapprove of Donald Trump's presidency.

7. What is the most significant shortcoming of the graphic?

  (a) At a glance, it appears like the approval percentage represents the American people as a whole rather than just Republicans (because "among Republicans" is in small font).

  (b) The percentage of people who neither approve nor disapprove is missing. This information is critical to having an unbiased graph in this scenario.

  (c) The disapprove bar is not present in the graph, despite there being 9% of Republicans who disapprove of Donald Trump's job as president.

Exercises 8 – 9 refer to the graphic in Figure 3.1.5.

Figure 3.1.5

8. Give two of the shortcomings of the graphic in Figure 3.1.5?

9. The graph in Figure 3.1.5 displays the number of appellate judgeships confirmed during each of the listed presidents' first congressional term. Which of the following graph types would be the most appropriate for this type of data?

    (a) A pie chart.

    (b) A line graph.

    (c) A bar graph.

10. What is the most significant shortcoming of this graphic on airline arrivals?

Accessed on 7/16/21 from https://www.theatlantic.com/national/archive/2011/11/airlines-most-likely-delay-your-flight/335108/.

3.2 Visualizing Data

The Excel worksheet VS_VFT Data of the workbook MtM_Unit2_CourseContent.xlsx contains VMI Fitness Test (VFT) data for over 1500 Cadets. The VFT was once administered to all cadets each semester, though currently it is only applicable to some cadets. Regardless, the data in this worksheet contains a lot of interesting information and will be used for a number of activities in this section. Today we focus on the heights of cadets.

1. Suppose that, after telling a friend you will attend VMI, she asks, "How tall are VMI cadets?" Is there a single correct answer to this question?

2. List some ways you could attempt to answer your friend's question using a single number.

3. When you use a single number to summarize the height of 1500 cadets, what kind of information is lost?

Table 3.1 shows one way to characterize the heights of the entire corps using just three numbers. The numbers in the second column are not heights but rather counts of the number of cadets whose height is within a range.

Range of Height	Number of Cadets
60" or less	14
61" to 77"	1501
78" or more	7

Table 3.1: Frequency Table of Heights Using 3 Bins

4. Table 3.1 summarized 1522 numbers into 3 numbers. Is this a useful summarization?

5. How could you make this table more useful? (*Hint:* If you're not sure, try to answer after finishing problem 12.)

Table 3.1 is an example of a *frequency table*. Frequency tables are used to summarize numeric data. Each row in a frequency table is called a *class* or a *bin*. Excel uses the term *bin*. Properties of classes or bins include:

- classes do not overlap,
- each data value falls into exactly one class, and
- each class has an upper and lower limit, with the possible exception of the first and last class.

Table 3.1 is an example where the first and last classes have no upper or lower limit.

The next frequency table uses a much smaller bin size.

Height	Number of Cadets
57	1
58	1
59	5
60	7
61	12
62	18
63	38
64	42
65	68
66	100
67	138
68	141
69	162
70	184
71	169
72	164
73	110
74	80
75	37
76	31
77	7
78	4
79	2
80	1

Table 3.2: Frequency Table of Height Using 23 Bins

6. How many cadets are at most five feet tall?

7. How many cadets are at least 6 1/2 feet tall?

8. How many cadets are within one inch of six feet?

9. What is a shortcoming with this table? How can you improve it? (*Hint:* What do you think of this choice of bin size?)

10. You should have recently read "Creating a Frequency Table With Excel" in Appendix A and created both a frequency and relative frequency table of cadet heights by gender. (If you have not yet completed this task, you should do so now before continuing.) Open this frequency table in Excel and change the bin size to 6. How many cadets are shorter than 63 inches?

11. Now change the bin size to 3. What percent of male cadets are 75" or taller?

12. Observe that in this case, five to nine classes or bins are reasonable to summarize cadet height. Can you think of a situation where it is appropriate to use a larger number of classes?

Suppose a friend from high school is at Virginia Tech. It happens that your friend is taking a statistics course and has created a frequency table of VT student heights similar to the one you just created for VMI. Your friend observes that VT has 11 students over 6'7" while VMI has only 1. Clearly, your friend claims, this demonstrates that VT students tend to be taller than VMI cadets.

Height Range (Inches)	Number of VT Students		Height Range (Inches)	Number of VMI Cadets
Less than 55	3		Less than 55	0
55 to 59	209		55 to 59	7
60 to 64	4803		60 to 64	117
65 to 69	10,818		65 to 69	609
70 to 74	8685		70 to 74	707
75 to 79	1235		75 to 79	81
More than 79	11		More than 79	1

Table 3.3: Frequency Table of Heights of VT Students and VMI Cadets

13. What do you think of your friend's claim? Is this a valid justification for claiming VA Tech students tend to be taller than VMI cadets?
    Multiple choice:

    (a) It's a valid claim because the tallest class of students determines which school has taller students.

    (b) It's a valid claim because if VT has more students in the "More than 79" category, then they have more students in every height category, and thus they are taller overall.

    (c) It's not a valid claim because the friend read the frequency table incorrectly.

    (d) It's not a valid claim because information about the tallest class doesn't give us an overall measure of heights of all students.

14. Table 3.3 displays counts of students in each range of height. How can you modify the table to make height comparisons between VT and VMI meaningful?

15. Recreate Table 3.3 in Excel, then replace the counts of students in the second and fourth columns with relative frequencies. Round your answers to 2 decimal places and use them to fill in Table 3.4.

Height Range (Inches)	% of VT Students		Height Range (Inches)	% of VMI Cadets
Less than 55			Less than 55	
55 to 59			55 to 59	
60 to 64			60 to 64	
65 to 69			65 to 69	
70 to 74			70 to 74	
75 to 79			75 to 79	
More than 79			More than 79	

Table 3.4: Relative Frequency Table of Heights of VT and VMI Cadets

16. What percent of VA Tech students are 6'3" or taller? What percent of VMI students are 6'3" or taller?

17. Does your friend still have strong evidence to support their claim?

18. Out of a group of 70 VMI cadets, how many would you expect to be shorter than 5'5"?

19. VMI has a much larger percentage of students 70 to 74 inches tall and a smaller percentage of students 60 to 64 inches tall. Give a plausible reason for this difference. (*Hint:* Consider the defining characteristics of VMI that make it different from VT.)

20. Match each relative frequency table with one of the following subsets of the VMI corps of cadets.

Table A

Height (in.)	Percentage
56-60	3.91%
60-64	36.64%
64-68	46.20%
68-72	13.25%
72-76	0%
76-80	0%

Table B

Height (in.)	Percentage
56-60	0.06%
60-64	2.19%
64-68	22.75%
68-72	47.12%
72-76	25.61%
76-80	2.27%

Table C

Height (in.)	Percentage
56-60	0.53%
60-64	6.24%
64-68	26.22%
68-72	43.36%
72-76	21.81%
76-80	1.84%

Table D

Height (in.)	Percentage
56-60	0%
60-64	0%
64-68	0%
68-72	16.56%
72-76	73.25%
76-80	10.19%

Population	Table
VMI Men's Basketball Team	
Entire Corps of Cadets	
Female Cadets	
Male Cadets	

Histograms

A histogram is a graphical presentation (i.e., a bar graph) of the numerical information in a frequency or relative frequency table.

Height (in.)	Frequency
57-58	2
59-60	12
61-62	30
63-64	80
65-66	168
67-68	279
69-70	346
71-72	333
73-74	190
75-76	68
77-78	11
79-80	3
Total:	1522

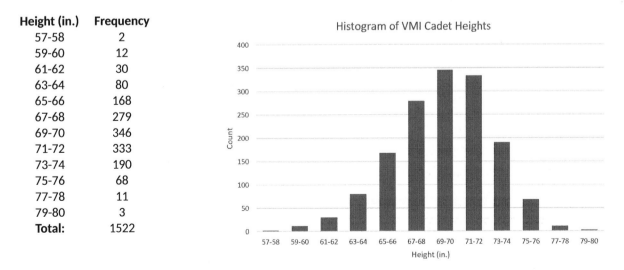

Figure 3.2.1: Frequency Table and corresponding Histogram

Each vertical bar in a histogram corresponds to a row in the frequency table. The height of the bar is proportional to the value of the corresponding number in the frequency table. The classes or bins of the frequency table appear as the ranges of data values in the bars of the histogram.

In Figure 3.2.1, it is easy to see that the bar labeled "61-62" represents the number of cadets with a height of 61" or 62". The simplicity of these labels is made possible by the fact that all heights are given in integers, without decimals.

Suppose heights were recorded with one decimal place of accuracy (such as, 68.2" instead of just 68"). The default pivot table generated by Excel will look different, as in Figure 3.2.2.

Height (in.)	Frequency
57-59	5
59-61	14
61-63	43
63-65	94
65-67	192
67-69	296
69-71	352
71-73	302
73-75	161
75-77	50
77-79	11
79-81	2
Total:	**1522**

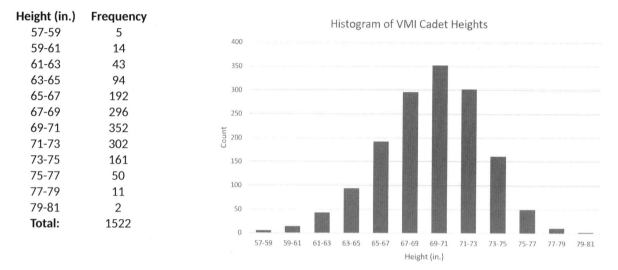

Figure 3.2.2: Frequency Table and corresponding Histogram

Notice how the ending value of each bin range is also the beginning value of the next bin range. The bin marked "61-63" will include all heights *greater than* 61" up to 63". Anyone with a height of 61.1" or 63.0" will be counted in this bin; anyone with a height of 61.0" will be counted in the previous bin.

Warning: If you create a histogram with bin width 5 using the Insert > Chart > Histogram options in Excel, you will get a different result than you would by making a histogram with bin width 5 using the pivot table and pivot chart as described in Appendix B, "Creating a Histogram using Excel." This is because the Excel histogram chart defines the lower and upper limits differently. While the Histogram tool of Excel is useful, pivot tables and pivot charts are often a better choice.

The Shape of Data

Every data set has a *distribution*, which can be described by characteristics such as its *shape, center,* and *spread*. We will explore these characteristics by looking at histograms.

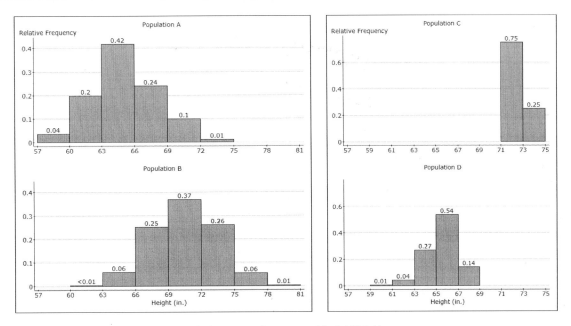

Figure 3.2.3: Histograms of Cadet Height

21. Which populations in Figure 3.2.3 have a bell-shaped curve?

A, B, D

22. Estimate the center of each population in Figure 3.2.3. We haven't defined *center* yet. We will, but in the meantime, it is instructive to let your intuition guide you. Mark a vertical line at what feels like the center of the data.

23. We will also define *spread* soon, but for now, think of it as a measure of how much the data differs, on average, from the center.

    (a) Which population has the greatest spread? B

    (b) Which population has the least spread? C

Notice that bin labels in Figure 3.2.3 are given in a different form than those in Figures 3.2.1 and 3.2.2. Only single numbers are given in Figure 3.2.3 instead of a range. This is commonly done, and in such cases we use the convention that bins are identified by their lower limits. The second bin in the histogram for Population A shows heights greater than or equal to 60" and less than 63". Recall that in Figure 3.2.2 that the bins were identified by their upper limits; that is, the bin marked "61-63" included heights of 63", but not 61".

One can use either convention, as long as it is clear to the reader. At the same time, if one is reading a histogram and the author didn't make it clear what convention is being used, it probably does not matter. In Population A of Figure 3.2.3, we can easily see that 42% of the population has a height between 63" and 66"; we likely do not need to know if this includes people with a height of exaclty 63" or 66".

24. (a) What percent of population A is shorter than 66 inches? 66

    (b) What percent of population B is 72 inches or taller? 25%

25. VMI companies were once assigned predominately according to height. Cadets in Alpha company were tall, cadets in Bravo company were not quite as tall, etc., with Delta and Echo companies composed of the shortest cadets, where heights increased back up through Hotel and India companies.

With this in mind, match the histograms in Figure 3.2.3 with the following VMI populations.

VMI Cadets	Histogram
Members of Alpha Company	
All Female Cadets	
Members of Delta Company	
All Male Cadets	

Bell-shaped histograms represent *normal* distributions. The data in a normal distribution is clustered around a single value in a symmetric fashion, like the middle picture in Figure 3.2.4.

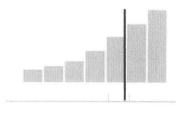  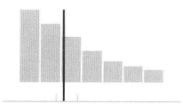

Skewed Left
(Negative Skew)

Symmetric

Skewed Right
(Positive Skew)

Figure 3.2.4: Shapes of Distributions

Another common shape for distributions is *skew*. Skew distributions are not symmetric and can be skewed left or right, as shown in Figure 3.2.4. We say that a distribution that is skewed left has a *tail* on the left, and a distribution that is skewed right has a tail on the right.

26. The histogram in Figure 3.2.5 shows that the distribution of women's pull-ups is skew. Is the distribution skewed left or right?

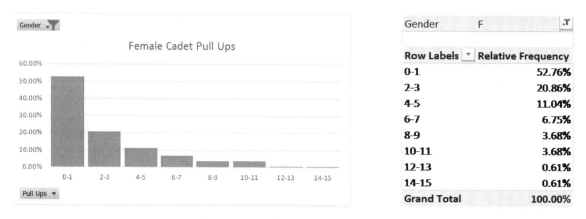

Figure 3.2.5: Pull-ups for Female Cadets

27. How many pull-ups puts a woman in the top 5% of women?

28. What is the approximate center for the distribution of women's pull-ups?

In Figure 3.2.6, the data values are spread roughly evenly across the range of heights. Each bar of the histogram is approximately the same height. In this case, we say the distribution is *uniform*.

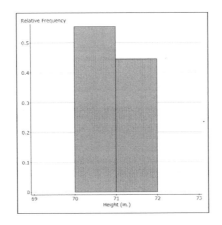

Figure 3.2.6: Heights of Men in Bravo Company

29. Which of the following data sets would have a uniform distribution?

    (a) the number of cadets by birth month

    (b) cadet weights

    (c) cadet SAT scores

Not all distributions are normal, skew, or uniform, but these three types occur frequently. The VFT data offers examples of each.

30. Assume that math test scores are uniformly distributed between 60 and 90. Draw a sketch of the relative frequency histogram of this distribution, and draw a vertical line approximating the center. Can you think of a general rule for the center of a uniformly distributed set of data?

31. Suppose you are an economist studying annual family income in the United States. You have data from over 100,000 families and the annual incomes range from $150 to $25,000,000. Draw a sketch of the histogram of this data. Don't attempt to be precise. You are only capturing the shape, spread, and center of the distribution.

32. What distribution would have the greatest amount of spread?

    (a) SAT scores of MIT students

    (b) SAT scores of the general population

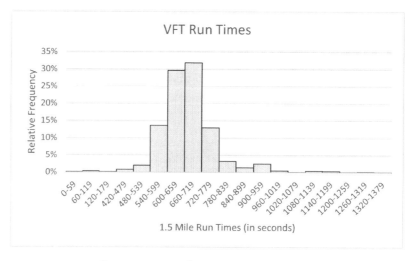

Figure 3.2.7: 1.5 Mile Run Times with Outliers

33. Examine the histogram in Figure 3.2.7. Recall that the x-axis values are the numbers of seconds to complete a 1.5 mile run. When you first look at it, what stands out visually? What data values look suspicious?

Now consider the revised histogram in Figure 3.2.8, where the unrealistic data values on the left in Figure 3.2.7 have been removed.

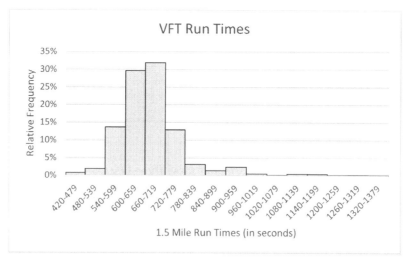

Figure 3.2.8: Time for 1.5 Mile Run without Outliers

34. Using Figure 3.2.8, find the percentage of the corps of cadets who completed the 1.5 mile run between 10 and 13 minutes.

35. If you want to complete the 1.5 mile run faster than 97% of the corps, what is the maximum amount of time you can take?

Knowing when it's ok to remove values from a data set, as we did in Figure 3.2.8, is a bit of an art. But here we can be confident the decision is sound because it is highly unlikely anyone ran 1.5 miles in less than 180 seconds.

When data values do not fit the general trend of the data, we say they are *outliers*. The unrealistic data values on the left in Figure 3.2.7 are outliers because they do not fit the trend of data for realistic 1.5 mile running times. In Section 3.5 we revisit the concept of outliers again.

Review and Reflect

Take a moment to think back on this section. What were the main ideas? What did you find most interesting?

-

-

-

-

-

Visualizing Data Summary

- A *frequency table* summarizes numeric data by dividing data values into distinct *classes* or *bins* and showing the total number of data points in each class.

- A *relative frequency table* shows the percentage of data in each class instead of the number of data points in a class.

- A *histogram* is a graphical presentation of the numerical information in a frequency or relative frequency table.

  - It is typically useful to experiment with the number of bins for a histogram (usually between 5 and 20) to arrive at a presentation that depicts the data in a meaningful way.

  - In this text, if bins are marked by ranges with repeating values (such as 0-5, 5-10, 10-15, etc.), we adopt the convention that the upper limit is included in the bin count.

  - In this text, if bins are marked by a single value (such as 0, 5, 10, etc.), we adopt the convention that the number defines the lower limit of the bin, and that value is counted with the bin.

- Every data set has a *distribution* that can be described by characteristics such as *shape*, *center* and *spread*.

- Common distribution shapes are *normal*, *skew*, and *uniform*.

  - Normal distributions are symmetric and data is clustered around a single point.

  - Skew distributions are not symmetric and can be *skewed left* with a left *tail*, or *skewed right* with a right tail.

  - Uniform distributions have histograms where all bars are roughly the same height and the overall distribution shape is approximately rectangular.

- A data point that does not fit the general trend of the data set is called an *outlier*.

  - Often outliers appear in data through errors when recording data.

  - Outliers can also appear without a mistake being made; they are just highly unusual values that do not fit a trend.

Exercises 3.2

Complete the step-by-step guide *Creating a Frequency Table With Excel* found in Appendix A, then answer the questions found in Exercises 1 – 9.

1. Where does the data appear to be concentrated?

    (a) Around 62-66 inches.

    (b) Around 67-71 inches.

    (c) Around 72-76 inches.

    (d) Around 67-76 inches.

2. How many cadets are between 67-71 inches tall?

    (a) 39

    (b) 755

    (c) 794

    (d) 52.17

3. What percent of males are at least 72 inches tall?

    (a) 27.73%

    (b) 28.65%

    (c) 31.94%

    (d) 43%

4. Using a bin size of 8, what percent of female cadets are 65-72 inches tall?

5. Using a bin size to 1, which height class contains the highest percentage of male cadets?

6. Using a bin size of 2, is the center of the data set roughly to the right or left of the 70 inch height class?

7. Which of the following best describes the shape of the histogram?

    (a) More data seems concentrated to the right.

    (b) More data seems concentrated to the left

    (c) The data is roughly symmetric.

    (d) The data seems to be roughly the same height throughout.

8. Using a bin size of 10, which of the following best describes the shape of the new histogram?

    (a) More data seems concentrated to the right.

    (b) More data seems concentrated to the left

    (c) The data is roughly symmetric.

    (d) The data seems to be roughly the same height throughout.

9. Change the bin size to a few different values. Based on your observations, which of the following statements makes the most sense?

    (a) A small number of bins (i.e. 2-4) best summarizes the data because most of the data falls into one or two large classes.

    (b) A large number of bins (i.e. 10 or more) best summarizes data, because the data is spread out across many heights. Having more classes means you can see almost every data point on your pivot table.

    (c) Using 5-9 bins best summarizes the data, because you can easily see the shape of the data without having too many classes.

Exercises 3.2

T-shirts are to be ordered for cadets, and Auxiliary Services knows that t-shirt size roughly correlates with height. In Exercises 10 – 11 use the worksheet VS_VFT Data **of** MtM_Unit2_Course Content.xlsx **to answer the given questions. (It will help to have completed the step-by-step guide** Creating a Frequency Table With Excel **found in Appendix A.)**

10. Complete the following table by creating relative frequency tables of cadet height, by gender. (Note: there are multiple ways to collect the data needed for this table, though one *cannot* easily create one table in Excel that matches the needed table exactly.)

	Uniform Size	Height Range	Percent of Corps (by gender)
Female	Small	63" or shorter	
	Medium	64" to 67"	
	Large	68" and taller	
Male	Small	64" or shorter	
	Medium	65" to 72"	
	Large	73 to 76"	
	X-Large	77" and taller	

11. Suppose that you find out that there are 258 women and 1464 men in the incoming class of cadets. Fill out the following table with estimates on the total number of t-shirts in each size that should be ordered rounding your answers to the nearest whole number.

	Uniform Size	Height Range	Number of Uniforms
Female	Small	63" or shorter	
	Medium	64" to 67"	
	Large	68" and taller	
Male	Small	64" or shorter	
	Medium	65" to 72"	
	Large	73 to 76"	
	X-Large	77" and taller	

Exercises 12 – 14 describe activities given in MA101_ExtraPractice.xlsx **on creating histograms from large data sets.**

12. The sheet VS_Histogram1_Problem gives the date and magnitude of over 23,000 worldwide earthquakes since 1965, and asks for histograms on the magnitude and year.

13. The sheet VS_Histogram2_Problem gives the GDP per capita of all world nations in US dollars, and asks for a histogram of the GDP data. The shape of the data gives understanding to the worldwide distribution of wealth.

14. The sheet VS_Histogram3_Problem has over 24,000 records of goals scored during European soccer matches and asks for a histogram on the time goals are scored.

3.3 Measures of Center

The Excel worksheet VS_VFT Data of the workbook MtM_Unit2_CourseContent.xlsx contains VMI Fitness Test (VFT) data for over 1500 Cadets. The VFT was once administered to all cadets each semester, though currently it is only applicable to some cadets. You will use this worksheet for a number of activities in this section, focusing on the heights of Cadets as done in the previous section.

Recall that when you planned your cultural trip in Section 1.2, you looked up the average daily high temperature for the month of your visit. That was enough to plan the clothing for your trip. It probably would not been useful to see the entire data set of all the temperature measurements from which this number was computed. That is, the "average daily high temperature" was a sufficient summary of all the data to plan clothing.

It is often useful to describe an entire distribution of data with a single number. That number is often chosen to represent "the middle," or "center," of the data. This section explores two of these *measures of center*, the mean and the median.

The Mean and the Median

One measure of the center of a data set is the *mean*. For a data set, the mean is the sum of all the data values, divided by the number of pieces of data. (This is often called the *average*, though that term sometimes refers to any measure of center. In this text, we'll avoid the word "average" and specify the *mean* or the *median*.)

Consider the data set of values 1, 2, 3, 6, 8; the mean is

$$\frac{1+2+3+6+8}{5} = 4.$$

1. Consider data sets A and B.

Data Set	Values					Mean
	x_1	x_2	x_3	x_4	x_5	$\bar{x}$
A	-2	-1	0	1	2	
B	0	0	0	0	100	

Table 3.5: Sample Data Sets

   (a) Complete the table by finding the means.

   (b) Is the mean of a data set always one of the values in that data set?

   (c) In which data set does the mean correspond more to your intuitive sense of what the center should be?

   (d) In which data set is the mean a poor measure of center?

   (e) What is true about the data in B that makes the mean misleading?

Another measure of the center of a data set is the *median*. The median is the middle value of the data set, when the data is put in increasing order.

Consider the data set of values 1, 2, 3, 6, 8; the median is 3.

In the previous example, the data set had an odd number of values, so the median was the middle number of the set. If a data set has an even number of values, we find the mean of the two middle numbers to get the median.

Consider the data set of values -1, 5, 7, 8, 10, 10; the median is

$$\frac{7+8}{2} = 7.5.$$

2. Sort the data sets A and B and find the medians.

Data Set	Values					Median
A	7	8	1	3	5	
A (sorted)						
B	7	8	1	5		
B (sorted)						

Table 3.6: Computing Medians

3. (a) If there are 24 cadets in your class and the median height is 68", can you determine how many cadets are shorter than 68"?

   (b) Why is your answer to (a), "No"?

   (c) If there are 24 cadets in your class and the median height is 68", describe how many cadets are shorter than 68" using phrases like "at most" and "at least." Similarly, how many cadets are taller than 68"?

   (d) Do your answers in (c) change if there are 25 cadets in your class?

The definition of the median establishes that it is a "middle" value in a set of data. Our intuition tells us that half of the data should be less than the median, and half of the data should be greater than the median. Question #3 above shows that sometimes this intuition fails. However, it is important to recognize that this intuition *is the right way to think about the median*. In a large data set, the percentage of data less than the median will be very close to 50%, and we won't be concerned with whether the true percentage is 49%, 49.5%, or 49.9%, etc.

Open the VS_VFT Data.xlsx worksheet in MtM_Unit2_CourseContent.xlsx. Excel uses the command AVERAGE to compute the mean, and the command MEDIAN to compute the median. (You may choose to use Excel's help files or the internet to learn more.)

4. Use the Excel functions to calculate the mean and median for cadet heights.

Comparing Measures of Center

Data Set	Values					Mean	Median
	x_1	x_2	x_3	x_4	x_5		
A	−2	−1	0	1	2		
B	0	0	0	0	10		

Table 3.7: Computing Means and Medians

5. Complete Table 3.7.

   (a) Does the mean or the median provide a better measure of center for data set B?

(b) Can we conclude that two data sets are similar if they have the same median?

6. Table 3.8 is the same as Table 3.7 except that the largest value in each data set has been replaced by a much larger value.

   (a) Complete Table 3.8.

   (b) Compare the new means and medians to those in Table 3.7. Which changed more drastically, the means or the medians?

Data Set	Values					Mean	Median
	x_1	x_2	x_3	x_4	x_5		
A	-2	-1	0	1	100		
B	0	0	0	0	100		

Table 3.8: Computing Means and Medians with Outliers

7. Consider the data sets in Table 3.9

   (a) What are the outliers in each data set A, B, and C ?

   (b) Find the means and medians for A, B, and C and complete the table.

   (c) Do outliers generally have a greater impact on the mean or the median?

   (d) Why don't the outliers in data set C affect the mean?

Data Set	Values					Mean	Median
	x_1	x_2	x_3	x_4	x_5		
A	-200	-1	0	1	2		
B	-2	-1	0	1	200		
C	-200	-1	0	1	200		

Table 3.9: Computing Means and Medians with Outliers

8. Suppose we replace the largest value in a data set with a larger number.

   (a) Does the mean increase, decrease, or remain unchanged?

   (b) Does the median increase, decrease, or remain unchanged?

   (*Hint:* Your answers to problem 6 might be helpful.)

The answer to part (a) in the last problem is especially important when the replacement number is not only larger, but an outlier. The mean may lose relevance as a measure of center.

9. Suppose we replace the smallest value in a data set with a smaller number.

   (a) Does the mean increase, decrease, or remain unchanged?

   (b) Does the median increase, decrease, or remain unchanged?

Again, the answer to part (a) in the previous problem is important because an outlier may make the mean a less useful measure of center for that data set.

10. Based on your answers to problem 8 and problem 9, write a sentence describing one benefit of the median over the mean as a measure of center.

The Shape of Data, Revisited

Now that we are working with defined notions of measures of center, let's revisit the relationship between the shape and center of a distribution. The following histograms show VMI cadet heights.

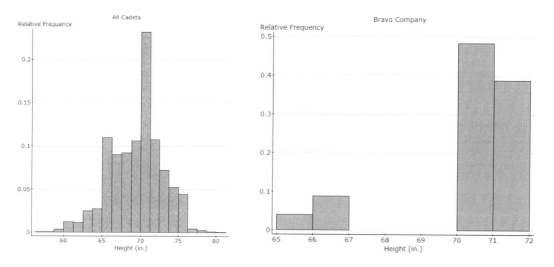

Figure 3.3.1: Histograms of Cadet Heights

11. (a) How would you describe the two histograms above: normal, skew, uniform, or other?

    (b) How would you describe the histogram below: normal, skew, uniform, or other?

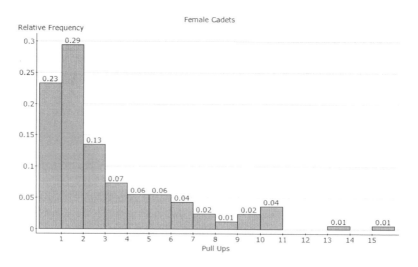

Figure 3.3.2: Histogram of Female Pull Ups

12. The mean of female pull ups is 2.57. By looking at the histogram in Figure 3.3.2, how can you tell that the median is 1?

13. Draw a vertical line on the histogram for female pull-ups that separates the bins for 0, 1, and 2 pull-ups from the bins for 3 or more pull-ups.

14. What percent of women do fewer than three pull-ups?

In the histogram of all cadets in Figure 3.3.1, recall the mean is 69.4" and the median is 70". Suppose we select a cadet at random from this distribution. If we don't have any further information about who was selected, both the mean and median are reasonable guesses for their height.

15. Now consider selecting a female cadet at random. Would the mean or median be a better predictor of the number of pull-ups she can do?

16. Is the mean a better predictor for height or pull-ups?

17. What is the relationship between the shapes of the height and pull-up distributions and their ability to predict values using the mean?

18. Do the outliers in the female pull-ups distribution affect the mean?

19. Complete each sentence with either "increase" or "decrease."

   (a) Outliers in the left tail of a distribution _____ the mean.
   (b) Outliers in the right tail of a distribution _____ the mean.

Skewed-Left

Skewed-Right

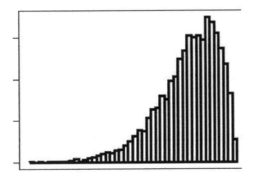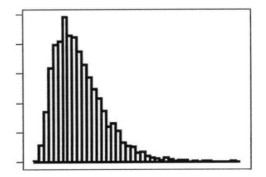

Figure 3.3.3: Skewed Distributions

20. Complete each sentence with either "more" or "fewer."

   (a) A distribution that is skewed left has _____ data points below the mean than above the mean.
   (b) A distribution that is skewed right has _____ data points below the mean than above the mean.

   answer

   (a) fewer

   (b) more

When we think of the center of a data set, we often think of the mean (which we usually call "the average"). This is fine when our data set has a symmetric distribution (normal or uniform). However, the mean is greatly affected by skewed distributions, being pulled in the direction of the skew.

While less commonly used in many parts of life, the median is a better measure of center for skewed data sets, and many important data sets are skewed. When reporting news on income or housing prices, the median is almost always used. There are often very high incomes, or very expensive houses, that can pull the mean up higher than what most would consider a "good" measure of center.

Review and Reflect

Take a moment to think back on this section. What were the main ideas? What did you find most interesting?

-

-

-

-

-

Measures of Center Summary

- The *mean* of a finite data set is the sum of all data values, divided by the number of values (what is commonly called "the average").

- The *median* of a data set with an odd number of values is the middle value when the set is ordered. If the data set has an even number of values, the *median* is the average of the middle two values when the set is ordered.

- Both the mean and median summarize a distribution with a single number; the units of that number are the same as the units of the data set.

- When a data set is symmetric (or nearly), the mean and median are close, and the mean is often used as the measure of center.

- In a skewed distribution, the median is usually a better measure of center because it is unaffected by outliers.

Exercises 3.3

1. True or False: The mean of a data set is always one of the values in that data set.

2. True or False: The median of a data set is always one of the values in that data set.

3. When is the mean a poor measure of center? (Choose all that apply.)

   (a) When there are many values in the data set.

   (b) When the data set contains both negative and positive values.

   (c) When the data set contains outliers.

   (d) When the data set contains large numbers.

   (e) When the data is skewed.

4. A data set has 1001 values. How many of these values are used to calculate the mean?

5. A data set has 1001 values. Assume they are sorted in ascending order. How many of these values are used to calculate the median?

6. A data set has a uniform distribution. Which of the following is likely true?

   (a) The mean is likely greater than the median.

   (b) The mean is less than the median.

   (c) The mean is nearly equal to the median.

7. A data set has a normal distribution. Which of the following is likely true?

   (a) The mean is likely greater than the median.

   (b) The mean is less than the median.

   (c) The mean is nearly equal to the median.

8. A data set has a skew-left distribution. Which of the following is likely true?

   (a) The mean is likely greater than the median.

   (b) The mean is less than the median.

   (c) The mean is nearly equal to the median.

9. A data set has a skew-right distribution. Which of the following is likely true?

   (a) The mean is likely greater than the median.

   (b) The mean is less than the median.

   (c) The mean is nearly equal to the median.

10. A data set has 1000 values. How many of these values are used to calculate the median?

11. A house-flipper is looking at purchasing a fixer-upper home. His real estate agent gives the selling price of comparable homes to help him estimate the resale value of his house once it is remodeled, shown in the table.

Street Name	Home Price (Thousands of $)
Walker St.	149
Campbell St.	135
Massie St.	174
Lewis St.	185
McCorkle Dr.	235.5
Hook Ln.	155

   (a) Find the mean and median home price.

(b) Would the mean or median of the given data be a better measure of center? Why?

12. Create a four-number data set where the median is 5 and the mean is 10.

13. Create a 4-number data set where the median is 5 and the mean is 0.

14. A college teacher always reports the average grade to her students when returning tests. On a recent test, two students admittedly don't try and earn grades significantly lower than the rest of the class.

   (a) If the teacher uses all scores to calculate a measure of center, would the mean or the median give the higher grade?

   (b) Since the two students admit to not trying, the teacher decides to not include their grades when computing a measure of center. Will this increase the mean, the median, or both?

Exercises 15 – 16 refer to the histograms shown below.

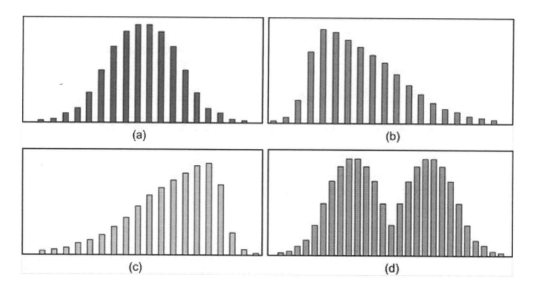

15. List all histograms in which the mean separates the distribution into two portions with approximately the same number of data values.

16. List all histograms in which there are more data values to the left (below) the mean than to the right (above) the mean.

3.4   Measures of Variation

We have investigated the mean and median as measures of center, and we have seen how each summarizes a distribution with a single number. But neither gives any information about the variability of the data. Consider the two histograms in Figure 3.4.1 showing heights for Alpha and Bravo cadets on the left and heights of all male cadets on the right. Note that the two groups of cadets have similar mean heights but very different distribution shapes. The difference in shape is not reflected by any measure of center but rather by *spread*, or *variation*.

In this section we explore three different measures of variation: the standard deviation, the range, and the interquartile range.

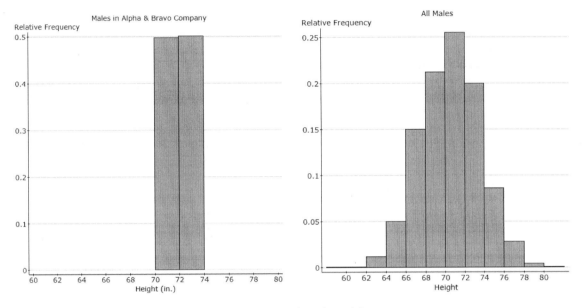

Figure 3.4.1: Male Cadet Height

1.   (a) How do the shapes of the two histograms compare? Is each best described as normal, skewed, or uniform?

uniformed   bell

   (b) How do the centers of the two histograms compare?

70   72

   (c) Which histogram shows a greater variation in heights?

2nd

The four distributions in the next figure were generated to create examples of distributions with different characteristics. They do not correspond to data in the VFT spreadsheet.

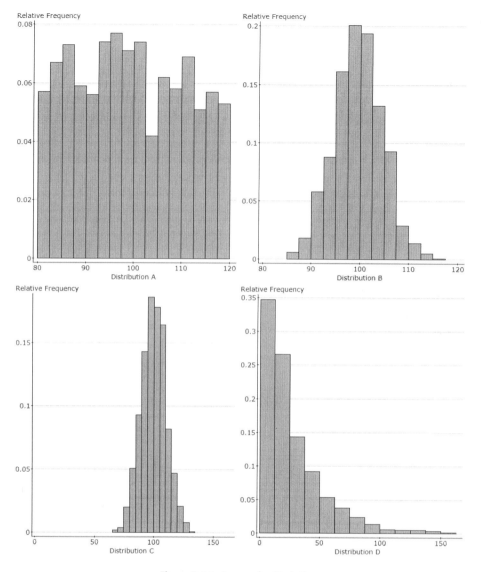

Figure 3.4.2: Comparing Variation

Variation is related to how much data values differ from the mean. When looking at a histogram, we evaluate variation by how much data values are clustered around the mean. A large variation indicates data values fluctuate a lot around the mean. A small variation means data values do not differ from the mean by much.

2. Which distribution has more variation: A or B?

3. Which distribution has more variation: C or D?

Standard Deviation

The *standard deviation* is a single number that measures the amount of variation in a data set. It essentially measures the mean distance the data is from the mean. (That description is accurate, though often confusing at first.) The larger the standard deviation, the larger the amount of variation within the data.

In this text we *will not* be learning a formula for computing the standard deviation, as we did for the mean and median. Rather, we'll let technology compute the standard deviation of a data set for us, and we'll focus on understanding what that number tells us.

Figure 3.4.3 uses the VFT data set and shows heights for female cadets, male cadets, and all cadets.

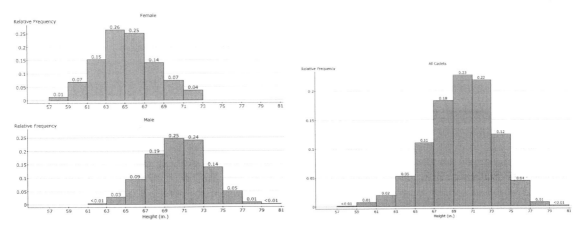

Figure 3.4.3: VMI Cadet Height

4. Considering each histogram in Figure 3.4.3, and using your knowledge of the corps of cadets, predict:

   (a) which histogram has the largest standard deviation, and
   (b) which histogram has the smallest standard deviation.

   male height

5. We can compute the mean and standard deviation of male and female cadet heights using Excel. Instructions for using Pivot Tables to compute these statistics are given in Appendix C. (It is highly beneficial to learn how to use Pivot Tables to perform these types of tasks.) Fill out the table below using either your work from Excel, or using the information given at the end of Appendix C. (Round your answers to one decimal place.)

	Height	
	Mean	**Standard Deviation**
Female		
Male		
Corps of Cadets		

Table 3.10: Standard Deviations of Height

6. We can use Excel to compute standard deviations without using a Pivot Table. Excel provides the function "STDEV.S" that computes the standard deviation. (The ".S" stands for "sample", whereas a "STDEV.P" is for "population". We'll use the ".S" version always.) To compute the standard deviation of all the heights, we can use the command "=STDEV.S(L2:L1523)", as all heights are in Column L.

Enter this command in a blank cell of your worksheet. Does the standard deviation given match your answer in Table 3.10 exactly?

7. Means and standard deviations have the same units as the data values. What are the units of the means and standard deviations in Table 3.10?

Now let's study the variation in the number of pull-ups from the VFT data. We begin by considering some histograms in Figure 3.4.4.

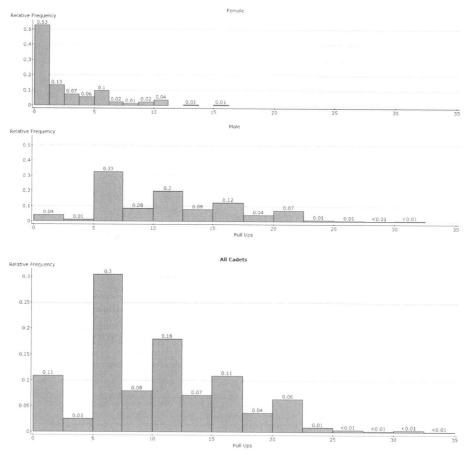

Figure 3.4.4: VMI Cadet Pull-ups

8. Referring to Figures 3.4.3 and 3.4.4, which do you predict has greater variation: height or pull-ups? (Note that we are comparing the standard deviations of different categories with different units; a standard deviation of 5 pull ups may mean something more/less significant than a standard deviation of 5 inches.)

9. Use the VFT data set, found in the worksheet VS_VFT Data of the workbook MtM_Unit2_CourseContent.xlsx, to compute the statistics in Table 3.11. Include units.

Pull-Ups

	Mean	Standard Deviation
Female		
Male		
Corps of Cadets		

Table 3.11: Mean and Standard Deviations of Pull-ups

10. Complete the table by entering the values and units of each statistic.

	Mean	Standard Deviation
Height (all cadets)		
Pull-Ups (all cadets)		

Did you predict that pull-ups have greater variation than height? The numbers in the previous table clearly show that the standard deviation of pull-ups, 6.01, is larger than the standard deviation of height, 3.42.

11. Do you think it makes sense to compare the standard deviation of pull-ups with the standard deviation of height? (*Hint:* Consider the units in each case.)

12. We have only seen examples where the standard deviation is a positive number. Can it be negative? Zero? (*Hint:* Recall that the standard deviation measures an average of distances from the mean)

Range

Our second measure of a data set's variation is the *range*. The range is the difference between the largest and smallest values in the data set. For example, the data set with values 6, 15, 3, 6, 8, 19, 23, has a range of 20 (i.e., $23 - 3 = 20$).

Unfortunately, Excel does not have a built-in range command. It does have MAX and MIN commands which find the largest and smallest value, respectively, in a set of data.

13. What is the range of pull-ups among all VMI cadets?

14. What is the range of heights among all VMI cadets?

15. What are the advantages and disadvantages of the range as a measure of spread?

16. Which measure of spread will outliers affect more: the range or the standard deviation?

The range is most useful when we know outliers do not exist within a data set, or when the range is small. Consider the heights of the male cadets in Alpha company: the range is 2". As the range is so small, there isn't "room" for any outliers. In practice, the range is usually only reported when any outliers have been removed from the data.

Interquartile Range

Our final measure of variation is the *interquartile range*. It combines the strengths of the range (easy computation, intuitive understanding) while removing the range's biggest weakness (the influence of outliers).

The interquartile range is the range of the middle 50% of the data. To understand this definition better, and in order to calculate the interquartile range, we need to first understand a few more concepts.

Recall that the median is the center value of a data set whose values are sorted from low to high, and that (roughly) 50% of the data is less than the median, and (roughly) 50% of the data is greater than the median. Because 50% of the data is less than the median, the median is also called the *50th percentile*.

We can define other percentiles in a similar fashion: 25% of the data in a data set is less than the "25th percentile", and 90% of the data is less than the "90th percentile", etc. The three most commonly used percentiles are the 25th, 50th, and 75th percentile. Figure 3.4.5 shows how these three percentiles break a data set into 4 equally-sized subsets. This has led to an alternate name for these percentiles, *quartiles*, as shown in Figure 3.4.5 and Table 3.12.

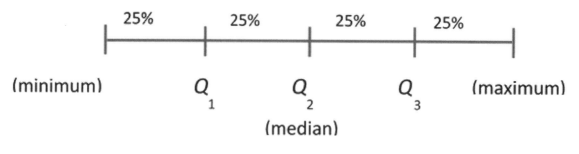

Figure 3.4.5: Quartiles

Percentile	Quartile
25th	Q1 or first quartile
50th	Q2 or second quartile
75th	Q3 or third quartile

Table 3.12: Percentiles and Quartiles

Recognize that 50% of the data fall between Q1 and Q3. Once we understand these terms, we understand how to compute the *interquartile range*, often abbreviated as IQR. It is defined as IQR = Q3−Q1.

Excel does have a quartile-computing function called QUARTILE.INC. Suppose your data is in column A, from cells 1 to 100. The commands in Table 3.13 demonstrate how to compute each quartile, including Q0 and Q4, the min and max, respectively.

Quartile	Excel Command
Q0 (the min)	QUARTILE.INC(A1:A100,0)
Q1	QUARTILE.INC(A1:A100,1)
Q2 (the median)	QUARTILE.INC(A1:A100,2)
Q3	QUARTILE.INC(A1:A100,3)
Q4 (the max)	QUARTILE.INC(A1:A100,4)

Table 3.13: Computing quartiles with Excel

(Note: the "INC" part of QUARTILE.INC stands for "inclusive"; Excel also has a command QUARTILE.EXC, where "EXC" stands for "exclusive". We aren't concerned with the difference here, but recognize that Excel has several functions with INC and EXC versions. We will always use the INC version.)

17. Use the VFT data set in Excel to complete Table 3.14.

	Corps of Cadets Pull-ups	Corps of Cadets Heights
Min		
Q1		
Median		
Q3		
Max		
Interquartile Range		

Table 3.14: Interquartile Ranges

18. On the same graph, sketch normal distributions with

   (a) Q1 = 50, Q2 = 100, Q3 = 150

   (b) Q1 = 90, Q2 = 100, Q3 = 110

19. Why is the IQR a measure of variation?

20. A large interquartile range indicates

   (a) greater variation

   (b) smaller variation

   (c) not enough information to say

Boxplots

A *boxplot* is a graph that shows the center, interquartile range, and full range of a distribution. Specifically, a boxplot shows the minimum, Q1, the median, Q3, and the maximum, so is sometimes called a *five-number summary*.

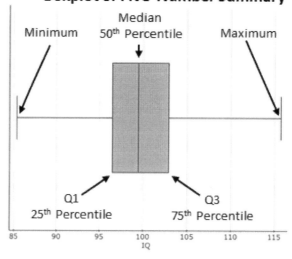

Figure 3.4.6: A Boxplot

The width of the shaded rectangle is the interquartile range, or the range of values between the 25th and 75th percentile. The vertical line inside the shaded rectangle is the median, or 50th percentile. The line extending left from the shaded rectangle ends at the minimum value and represents the lowest 25% of the data values. The line extending right from the shaded rectangle ends at the maximum value and represents the upper 25% of data values.
(Note: this box plot is graphed horizontally, though some software programs make box plots vertically by default.)

21. Use the statistics you computed in Table 3.14 to manually create a box plot for cadet pull-ups.

22. Use the statistics you computed in Table 3.14 to manually create a box plot for cadet heights.

23. Using the data in VS_VFT Data, use Excel to create a boxplot (Excel calls them Box & Whisker plots) of cadet heights. Note that Excel creates vertically-oriented plots by default. It also automatically looks for outliers, and signifies these with dots on the graph, and computes the quartiles without considering the outliers. It also marks the mean with an "X". These default settings can be changed if you desire, but it isn't necessary.

    Be sure your result makes sense compared to Table 3.14.

Review and Reflect

Take a moment to think back on this section. What were the main ideas? What did you find most interesting?

-

-

-

-

-

Measures of Variation Summary

- The standard deviation, range, and interquartile range are measures of the variation, or spread, of a distribution. Each of them summarizes the distribution with a single number.

- The *standard deviation* measures the distance, on average, the data in a distribution is from the mean.
    - It is never negative.
    - It may be zero, but only in the case where *all* the data values are the same.
    - It can be computed using Excel's STDEV.S command, or using a Pivot Table.

- The *range* is the difference between the largest and smallest values in the data set.
    - Outliers can make the range deceptively large.
    - Excel doesn't have a range function, but the range can be found by subtracting the output of the MAX and MIN functions.

- The *interquartile range*, or IQR, is the range of the middle 50% of the data. The IQR is generally not influenced by outliers.

- Percentiles are values where a certain percent of the data in a set is less than that value; if the 60th percentile in a data set is 200, then 60% of the values in the data set are less than 200.

- The 25th, 50th and 75th percentiles are given special names: the first, second and third quartiles (Q1, Q2 and Q3), respectively. Additionally,
    - the minimum value is called Q0, and the maximum value is Q4, and
    - the Excel function QUARTILE.INC can be used to compute quartiles.

- A *boxplot* (or *five-number summary* or *box-and-whisker plot*) is a simple graph showing the minimum, Q1, median, Q3, and maximum of a data set. The rectangle bounded by Q1 and Q3 is shaded to show the interquartile range.

Assignment: Is the World Getting Richer?

The Excel worksheet VS_WorldGDP of the workbook MtM_Unit2_CourseContent.xlsx contains information about the Gross Domestic Product (GDP) per capita for a multitude of counties. Economists from around the world study the economic output of each country by measuring the total amount of goods and services produced by that country in each year. This number, the GDP, is divided by the population to arrive a GDP per capita which is a measure of the wealth of citizens of that country.

You will analyze this data using the statistical tools we've developed so far to answer an interesting question: Is the world getting richer?

In a Word document, answer each of the numbered questions below, writing text and inserting graphs as needed.

Part 1: Shape of the Distribution

1. Predict the shape of the distribution (symmetric, skewed left, skewed right or uniform) for the GDP from the year 2000. Then create a histogram of the GDP for the year 2000 and state if your prediction matched the shape of the histogram. You won't be graded on whether or not your prediction is correct, but you will be graded on the professional appearance of your figures. This implies that each figure should have the appropriate title, labels and legend. If your figure contains colors be certain that the printed product you turn in also is in color.

2. Predict the shape of the distribution (symmetric, skewed left, skewed right or uniform) for the GDP from the year 2021. Then create a histogram of the GDP for the year 2021 and state if your prediction matched the shape of the histogram. (The same grading principles apply as did in #1.)

3. Scroll to the bottom of the table that contains the GDP data for each country. The last two rows contain the overall mean and median GDP per capita for each year are displayed. Since the median splits the distribution into two equal pieces, 50% of the countries are below the median GDP per capita and 50% are above. Calculate the percent of countries with a GDP per capita below the mean then complete the following table.

Excel hint: The GDP data worksheet is an Excel table and the first row contains the names of the data fields in the table. Notice that the first row (the names of the fields) has a different appearance. Left-click on the triangle on the right side of any cell to sort the whole table by that column. This can help you quickly count the number of countries less/greater than a particular value.

	Value	% of countries with lower GDP per capita	% of countries with greater GDP per capita
Mean (2014)			
Median(2014)			

4. Which measure of center is more appropriate to use for GDP per capita? Explain your answer.

Part 2: Is the world getting richer?

Scroll back to the bottom of the table where the mean and median GDP per capita for each year are displayed. Insert a new row above the row that contains the mean GDP and label this rows as Year and enter in the appropriate values.

Beneath the Median row add a row for the first quartile, labeled Q1, and the third quartile, labeled Q3. Use Excel commands to fill in the values for both rows. The first three entries should look like:

Zimbabwe	563	568	531
Year	**2000**	**2001**	**2002**
Mean	7917.1784	7828.38967	8569.92019
Median	1765	1839	2120
Q1	554	518	572
Q3	9566	8685	10651

5. We would like to look at this data using a scatter plot to better capture how the measures of center are changing over time. Make a scatterplot of all the data (and labels) in the rows Year, Mean, Median, Q1 and Q3. The horizontal axis should be the year and the vertical axis should be statistic's value. You will need to include a legend, since we are looking at several plots on the same graph.

   What does this chart show you about how the mean relates to other statistics?

6. Recreate a scatter plot graphing only the Year and Mean. Using this graph, does the world appear to be getting richer?

7. Recreate a scatter plot graphing only the Year, Median, Q1 and Q3. Using this graph, does the world appear to be getting richer?

8. Compare your answers from problems 6 and 7. Which of the two charts better describes the world's GDP per capita and why?

Exercises 3.4

1. List all of the following that are not measures of variation: Mean, Median, Standard Deviation, Quartile, Percentile, Interquartile Range.

2. List all of the following that always have the same units as the data values: Mean, Median, Standard Deviation, Quartile, Percentile, Interquartile Range.

3. The standard deviation of a set of data values is zero. What can you conclude must be true about the data? Choose all that apply.

   (a) The sum of the values in the data set equals zero

   (b) All of the data values are equal

   (c) The mean and median are equal

   (d) Nothing - the standard deviation can never be zero.

4. Which of the following statements are true about the standard deviation? Choose all that apply.

   (a) It is always greater than 0

   (b) If two data sets have the same standard deviation, then they have identical values

   (c) It has the same units as the mean

5. Which of the following groups will have the largest standard deviation in age?

   (a) Corps of Cadets

   (b) VMI Faculty

   (c) Residents in a retirement home

   (d) Attendees at a home football game

6. How much variation is there in a data set where all values are the same?

7. You are filling an open position in a research lab and want to hire the smartest person, as measured by IQ, for the job. You select the new hire by drawing a name from one of two bins that each contain the names of several candidates. You are told that the mean IQ of the candidates in each bin is 100. If your goal is to minimize the chance of hiring a person with an IQ less than 90, what additional statistic would you like to know for each bin?

   (a) Median

   (b) Standard Deviation

   (c) Additional information in not needed. I can choose from either bin because both have a mean IQ of 100.

   (d) The number of candidates in each bin

8. A friend wants a recommendation for a weight loss program. You research two programs and find the following statistics:
   Program A: mean weight loss = 20 lbs, standard deviation = 15 lbs
   Program B: mean weight loss = 25 lbs, standard deviation = 30 lbs
   Which program offers the most reliable results? Choose the best answer.

   (a) Program A because it has the smaller standard deviation.

   (b) Program A because it has the smaller mean.

   (c) Program B because it has the larger standard deviation.

   (d) Program B because it has a larger mean weight loss.

9. You calculated the standard deviation of your data set as -1.23. What can you be certain of?

   (a) Most of the data values are slightly smaller than the mean.

   (b) You made a mistake in your calculation. The standard deviation cannot be negative.

(c) The mean is less than the median.

(d) The mean of the values is also negative.

Exercises 10 – 16 use the VFT data found in the Excel worksheet VS_VFT Data **of the workbook** MtM_Unit2_CourseContent.xlsx.

10. What is the average number of situps by male cadets?

(a) 68.1

(b) 70.2

(c) 72.8

(d) 75.4

11. What is the standard deviation of the number of situps by female cadets?

(a) 15.7

(b) 16.1

(c) 18.8

(d) 19.1

12. What is the average run time score of female cadets?

(a) 67.2

(b) 73.1

(c) 78.1

(d) 85.8

13. What is the standard deviation of the run time score of male cadets?

(a) 15.2

(b) 16.7

(c) 17.3

(d) 18.4

14. What is the range of situp scores of all cadets?

(a) 60

(b) 68

(c) 75

(d) 110

15. What is the interquartile range of situp scores of all cadets?

(a) 7

(b) 8

(c) 15

(d) 35

16. What is the interquartile range of situp scores of only the cadets who passed the VFT?

(a) 9

(b) 10

(c) 13

(d) 16

17. What term best describes the shape of this distribution: Skewed Right, Skewed Left, Symmetric, or Uniform?

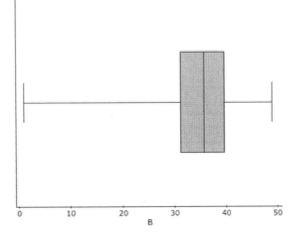

Use the following set of histograms and box-and-whisker plots in Exercises 18 – 20.

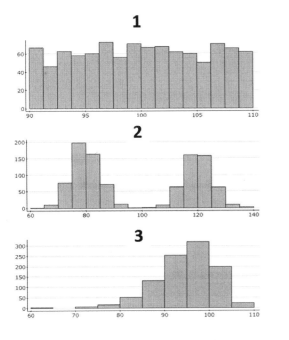

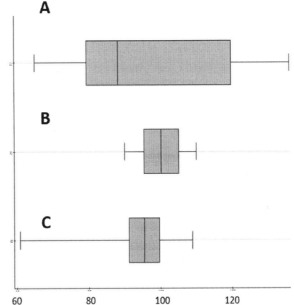

18. What box plot corresponds to histogram #1?

19. What box plot corresponds to histogram #2?

20. What box plot corresponds to histogram #3?

Exercises 21 – 22 use the Excel workbook MA101_ExtraPractice.xlsx.

21. The worksheet VS_CenterAndVariation1_Problem contains data on the price of conventional and organic avocados in various cities around the U.S., providing practice for creating histograms, computing means, standard deviations, quartiles, etc.

22. The worksheet VS_CenterAndVariation2_Problem contains data on the nutritional content of common breakfast cereals, providing practice for creating histograms, computing means and standard deviations, etc.

3.5 Measures of Relative Standing

The Excel worksheet VS_IQ Scores of the workbook MtM_Unit2_CourseContent.xlsx contains sample IQ scores for three groups of people and will be used to understand certain principles within this section.

Intelligence quotient, or IQ, scores are defined so that the mean IQ score is 100. Suppose a friend tells you her IQ score is 120. Is that impressive? Is 120 a slightly above-average score, or an unusually high score? To answer these questions, we need to know where 120 is *relative* to all other scores. If 120 is higher than most IQ scores, we will be impressed.

In this section, we will explore two measures of *relative standing*: measures of how one particular data value compares to the rest of the data set. If we know all of the data values in a data set, we can compute a *percentile* (which we briefly discussed in the previous section). Often we only know basic statistics about a data set, the mean and standard deviation. In those situations, we can compute a *z-score*, which can also indicate relative standing.

Percentiles

To know if 120 is a impressive IQ, it would help to know what percentage of the population has an IQ lower than 120. This percentage is defined as the percentile, and it is used to relate a specific value to the other data values in the population.

For instance, if we knew that the score of 120 was in "the 95th percentile", we'd know that a score of 120 was greater than 95% of all scores, and we'd likely be impressed. If we knew that the score of 120 was in "the 70th percentile", we'd know that the score of 120 was greater than 70% of all scores. While this is certainly good, it is not as impressive as the 95th percentile.

1. If you only know that a person's IQ is 120 and the mean of the population is 100, can you calculate the percent of people in the population with an IQ less than 120? If not, what other information do you need to know?

2. Sketch a histogram for a normal distribution with a mean of 100 where an IQ score of 120 looks unusually high compared to the population.

3. Sketch a histogram for a normal distribution with a mean of 100 where an IQ score of 120 does not look unusually high compared to the population.

4. In which of your two sketches does the distribution have the larger standard deviation?

5. In the following, circle the words "decreases,", "increases", "more" or "less" so that the statements are correct, assuming normally distributed IQ scores with mean 100.

   (a) As the standard deviation increases, the number of IQ scores above 120 decreases/increases.

   (b) As the standard deviation decreases, the number of IQ scores below 120 decreases/increases.

   (c) As the standard deviation increases, an IQ score of 120 becomes more/less unusual.

   (d) As the standard deviation increases, the percentile of an IQ score of 120 decreases/increases.

The term *unusually high* means something specific. We will say an IQ score in the 95th percentile or above is *unusually high*. That is, an unusually high score is greater than 95% of all scores. Similarly, an IQ score in the 5th percentile or below is *unusually low*.

Excel provides two functions that we'll use relating to percentiles. Suppose we have a data set in rows 1 through 1001 of column A. The command "=PERCENTILE.INC(A1:A1001,0.95)" finds the value that is in the 95th percentile of the data. The result will be a data value (not a percent).

Suppose we know a value, such as your friend's IQ score of 120, and want to know its percentile. We can use the PERCENTRANK.INC function, as in "=PERCENTRANK.INC(A1:A1001,120)". The result will be a decimal between 0 & 1. An answer such as 0.623 means the value is in the 62nd percentile.

(Note that Excel has ".EXC" versions of both functions, and as established before, we'll use the ".INC" versions.)

6. Open the Excel worksheet VS_IQ Scores and use the built-in statistical functions to complete Table 3.15, which is the same as Table 1 in the worksheet. (Note: once you determine the functions for the Blue column, you should be able to copy/paste, or click/drag, the formulas into the Green column.)

	Red	Blue	Green
Mean	99.18		
Standard Deviation	4.93		
Q1	96		
Median	99		
Q3	102		
Interquartile Range: Q3-Q1	6		
Unusually Low: 5th Percentile	91		
Unusually High: 95th Percentile	107		
Percentile of IQ = 120	N/A		

Table 3.15: IQ Score Statistics

7. In the Red group, what is the reason we were not able to find the percentile of an IQ of 120?

8. As the standard deviation increases, the 5th percentile IQ score

   (a) decreases

   (b) increases

   (c) does not change

9. As the standard deviation increases, the 95th percentile IQ score

   (a) decreases

   (b) increases

   (c) does not change

10. As the standard deviation increases, the percentile of an IQ score of 120

    (a) decreases
    (b) increases
    (c) does not change

11. Which population has more IQs above 120: Red, Blue or Green?

12. Which population has more IQs below 80: Red, Blue, or Green?

13. Which population has the most IQs in the range 95 to 105: Red, Blue, or Green?

14. Suppose you take an IQ test and your score is just below the 95th percentile so your IQ is not considered unusually high. Which change would make your IQ unusually high?

    (a) the standard deviation increases
    (b) the standard deviation decreases
    (c) the mean increases
    (d) none of the above because your score is unchanged

The previous questions demonstrate how the percentile is used as a measure of relative standing. Each IQ score in a data set has a corresponding percentile which is the percent of IQ scores that are lower. You can use an IQ score's percentile to see how it compares relative to all other IQs in the data set. You can then determine if an IQ score is unusually low or high by examining its percentile.

You cannot determine whether an IQ score is unusually high merely by observing how far it is above the mean. A person in the Red population with an IQ of 110 is above the 95th percentile and could justifiably claim to have an exceptional IQ. However, a person in the Green population with an IQ of 120 is only in the 85th percentile. That is better than 85% of the population but wouldn't be considered unusual.

Recall that we defined the term *outlier* when studying measures of center. Intuitively, the terms *outlier* and *un-usual value* feel similar, but we can see in Figure 3.5.1 they are not the same. The x-axis is housing square footage (in thousands) and the y-axis is housing prices (in hundred thousand dollars). The square data point does not fit the trend line, and is an outlier. However, a housing price of $400,000 is not unusually high, as there are a number of other houses that cost even more.

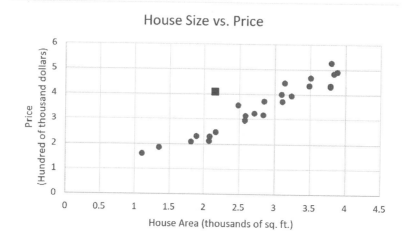

Figure 3.5.1: Housing Prices as a Function of Square Feet, illustrating an outlier

z-Scores

To calculate a percentile, you need to know all the data values. It would be nice to have a measure of relative standing that is simpler to calculate. There is such a measure using the mean, which we will call $\bar{x}$, and the standard deviation, which we will call s.

The first step is to calculate several deviations from the mean for each of the Red, Blue, and Green populations, using the statistics in Table 3.15. (Keep reading: don't fill in Table 3.16 yet.)

		Population		
		Red	**Blue**	**Green**
$\bar{x} - 2s$	**IQ Value**	89.32		
	Percentile	2.3		
$\bar{x} - 1s$	**IQ Value**	94.25		
	Percentile	16.9		
$\bar{x} + 1s$	**IQ Value**	104.10		
	Percentile	85.7		
$\bar{x} + 2s$	**IQ Value**	109.3		
	Percentile	98		

Table 3.16: Calculations with Means & Standard Deviations

Example: In the Red group, we found the mean was $\bar{x} = 99.18$ and the standard deviation was $s = 4.93$. Thus $\bar{x} - 2s = 99.18 - 2(4.93) = 89.32$, which we can enter into the top cell of the Red column. To find the percentile, we use the PERCENTRANK.INC function: =PERCENTRANK.INC(A2:A1001,89.32)=0.023. This means 89.32 is the 2.3rd percentile.

15. Fill in the rest of Table 3.16. (Again, complete the Blue column first, then copy your formulas to the Green column.)

16. If an IQ score is 2 standard deviations below the mean, then it is approximately in the _____ percentile.

17. If an IQ score is 2 standard deviations above the mean, then it is approximately in the _____ percentile.

18. Approximately what percent of the IQ scores in the Red, Blue, and Green populations are within 2 standard deviations of the mean?

19. Based on your calculations in Table 3.16, what is an alternate method to define unusually low or high values using just the mean and standard deviation?

The observations you made with the IQ score data sets indicate what happens in general for data that is normally distributed. If the data is normally distributed, then approximately 95% of the data values are within two standard deviations from the mean. With this in mind, we can also state that a value is unusually high/low if it is farther than 2 standard deviations from the mean.

It is useful to generalize this finding by introducing a new statistic, the z-score:

$$z\text{-score} = \frac{x - \bar{x}}{s}.$$

The z-score measures distance from the mean in units of standard deviations. Thus unusually high values are those with z-scores 2 and higher, and unusually low values are those with z-scores -2 and lower. Figure 3.5.2 summarizes how z-scores are used to mark the boundary between usual values and unusually low and high values.

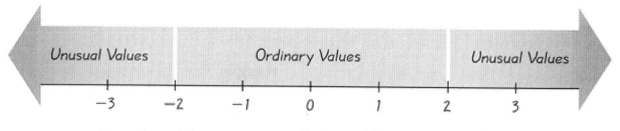

Standard Deviations Below/Above the Mean

Figure 3.5.2: Using z-scores to Determine Usual and Unusual Values

For example, in the Red population with mean 100 and standard deviation 5 (numbers rounded to make calculations easier), an IQ score of 110 has a z-score of:

$$z - \text{score} = \frac{110 - 100}{5} = 2,$$

and the IQ score of 110 would be considered unusually high.

However, the Green population with mean 100 and standard deviation 20 (again, numbers are rounded), an IQ score of 110 has a z-score of:

$$z - \text{score} = \frac{110 - 100}{20} = 0.5,$$

so the IQ score of 110 would not be considered unusually high.

20. Recall the Blue group has a mean IQ of 99.56 and standard deviation of 10.37.

    (a) What is the z-score of the IQ of 126?
    (b) What is the z-score of the IQ of 93?

Using z-Scores to Compare Items From Different Categories

If you are a sports fan, you probably have a favorite team and player and might argue with fellow sports fans over who is the best. Can you use statistics to settle an argument like this especially when it involves two different sports like basketball and baseball? For example, who was a better offensive player: Kobe Bryant, NBA player with the Los Angeles Lakers, or Derek Jeter, MLB player with the New York Yankees?

There are many statistics that people use to attempt to quantify the abilities of athletes, such as points per game (PPG) in basketball, or batting average (BA) in baseball. Perhaps you can think of others.

21. Can we compare PPG and BA directly? Explain.

In the previous question hopefully you stated reasons why you cannot directly compare Kobe Bryant's PPG with Derek Jeter's BA. Now consider ways you can compare Bryant's performance *relative to all NBA players* and Jeter's performance *relative to all MLB players*. In other words, since we cannot compare Bryant and Jeter's performance directly, we compare each player's performance relative to their peers.

Let's begin by examining the offensive performance, as measured by career average PPG, for all NBA players, past and present. The mean PPG of NBA players is 6.59 with a standard deviation of 4.94. Bryant's lifetime PPG is 22.9.

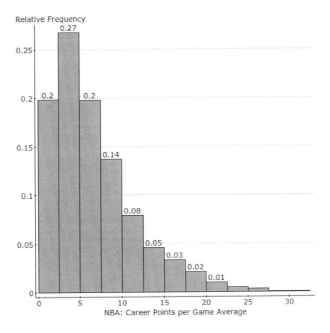

Figure 3.5.3: Histogram of NBA Lifetime Points-Per-Game Averages

22. Draw a vertical line in Figure 3.5.3 to mark the PPG two standard deviations above the mean. Approximately what percent of NBA players' PPG is below (to the left) of this mark?

23. Draw another vertical line in Figure 3.5.3 to mark Bryant's PPG on the histogram of PPG for all NBA players.

24. Estimate the percent of NBA players whose PPG is below Bryant and the percent above Bryant.

25. Use the previous results to write a sentence defending the position that Bryant was one of the greatest NBA players.

Now let's examine the performance, as measured by career average BA, for all MLB players, past and present. The mean BA of MLB players is .273 with a standard deviation of .026. Jeter's lifetime BA is .310.

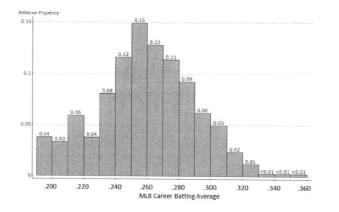

Figure 3.5.4: Histogram of MLB Lifetime Batting Averages

26. Draw a vertical line in Figure 3.5.4 to mark the BA two standard deviations above the mean. Approximately what percent of MLB players' BA is below (to the left) of this mark?

27. Draw another vertical line in Figure 3.5.4 to mark Jeter's BA on the histogram of BA for all MLB players.

28. Estimate the percent of MLB players whose BA is below Jeter and the percent above Jeter.

29. Use the previous results to write a sentence defending the position that Jeter was one of the greatest MLB players.

In the previous questions, you compared Bryant's PPG relative to the population of all NBA players and Jeter's BA relative to the population of all MLB players. Your goal is to compare Bryant, a basketball player, with Jeter, a baseball player, but a direct comparison is not possible. Instead, you can compare their relative positions in their respective populations. The player who is most unusual with respect to their population is the winner!

			NBA PPG		
	PPG x	Bryant's Percentile	Mean $\bar{x}$	Standard Deviation s	Bryant's z-score: $\dfrac{x - \bar{x}}{s}$
Bryant	22.9		6.59	4.94	

			MLB BA		
	BA x	Jeter's Percentile	Mean $\bar{x}$	Standard Deviation s	Jeter's z-score: $\dfrac{x - \bar{x}}{s}$
Jeter	.310		.273	.026	

Table 3.17: z-Scores for Bryant and Jeter

30. Fill in the percentile's we already calculated for Bryant and Jeter in Table 3.17. Then calculate the z-scores for Bryant and Jeter then complete the table above. Who is the better offensive player? Why?

Review and Reflect

Take a moment to think back on this section. What were the main ideas? What did you find most interesting?

-

-

-

-

-

Relative Standing Summary

- The *percentile* of a data value is the percentage of data that is lower than that value. A percentile is useful for understanding a data value relative to the entire data set.

  1. To find the value within a data set with a given percentile, use Excel's PERCENTILE.INC function.

  2. To find the percentile of a known value within a data set, use Excel's PERCENTRANK.INC function.

- We have two different measures of *unusually high/low*.

  - Data values in the 95th percentile or higher are unusually high; data values in the 5th percentile or lower or unusually low.

  - In data sets with normal distributions, data values that have a Z-score greater than 2 are considered unusually high; data values that have a Z-score less than -2 are considered unusually low.

- In statistics, "unusual" means something different than "outlier."

  - Data values can be outliers without being unusual.

  - Data values can be unusual without being outliers.

  - When analyzing a data set, outliers are often removed, though unusual values are not.

- A *z-score* measures distance from the mean in units of standard deviation and is computed using: z-score = $\frac{x - \bar{x}}{s}$ where $\bar{x}$ is the mean and s is the standard deviation.

Assignment: Cadet Company Fitness

Background:

VMI's superintendent has tasked you with determining which of four companies is most physically fit. Each cadet in each company participated in the VMI Fitness Test (VFT), which is composed of a 1.5 mile run, pull-ups, and number of sit-ups completed in 2 minutes. The scores of each event for each cadet is provided to you in the Excel worksheet `VS_Company Fitness` of the workbook `MtM_Unit2_CourseContent.xlsx`. The overall VFT score is the sum of the three scores. To prevent accusations of bias, the four companies are simply named A, B, C & D (not necessarily Alpha, Bravo, etc.) You are assigned to study the data using the statistical techniques you have learned thus far and prepare a written response to the superintendent. Your report should include an Executive Summary, an Introduction, Analysis, and a Conclusion.

Getting Started

- **Define "physically fit"**

    - How will you measure a cadet's physical fitness? Suppose James has run, sit-up and pull-up scores of 80, 80 and 80, respectively, and Jamaal has scores 90, 80, 70.

        You could add up these three scores (i.e., just use the VFT score) and conclude they are equally fit.

        You could decide that pull-ups are not important at all and just add the run and sit-up scores, meaning Jamaal is more fit.

        You could decide pull-ups are twice as important as the other two events, and give James the score of $80 + 80 + 2 * 80 = 320$ and Jamaal the score of $90 + 80 + 2 * 70 = 310$, meaning James is more fit.

        Of course, there are lots of other measures of physically fit available.

    - How will you measure a company's physical fitness? You could consider their measures of center: their mean or median scores. You could consider the number of cadets who performed unusually well and also unusually poorly. You can consider the distributions of scores for each company: uniform, normal, etc.

- **Analyze the data**

    - What tools would be helpful to understand the data? Excel can compute your fitness scores for you quickly; pivot tables and charts can help you quickly see means, medians, standard deviations, and histograms for each company. You can also create boxplots.

        It is not enough to just use mean company scores. The mean VFT score for each company is very similar, ranging from 236 to 241. There is not enough variation among those scores to strongly argue that one company is more fit than the others.

    - The selection of tools go hand in hand with your definition of a company's fitness. For instance, you may think you have a good definition of company fitness that points to Company A as being most fit. Then you create a boxplot of relevant data, and now you think Company B is more fit. It's ok to redefine "fitness" as you do your analysis.

Writing Your Report

- Your report is to be submitted as a Word document.

- **Executive Summary:** The report should begin with an Executive Summary (no more than 1 page). Anyone should be able to read this Summary and quickly understand the question, the answer, and the *basics* of what you did to answer the question, including how you measured cadet and company fitness. Do not give many details or calculations. Do not make the reader wait until the end of the Executive Summary to know which company is most fit.

    You should format your executive summary as a memo to the superintendent. Google "memo format" for ideas, but it should at least have To, From, and Regarding information.

- **Report:** This will contain three parts, and be between 1 and 3 pages long.

– In the Introduction, introduce and explain your definition of fit, provide context and background for this problem, and indicate the purpose of your analysis.

– In the Analysis section, present your finding using professional statistical graphs, tables, etc. (with proper labeling). State, with justification, any important assumptions inherent to your analysis.

  Again, it is insufficient to simply use means. You have learned about spread, skew, shape of distributions, standard deviation, quartiles, etc. Use these in your analysis.

– In the Conclusion, use your analysis to present the most fit company and defend this answer. Make sure to properly reference items in your Analysis section.

Exercises 3.5

In Exercises 1 – 4, suppose you have a data set of heights in the range A2:A2001 in an Excel worksheet.

1. Which of the following best explains the output of the function "=PERCENTILE.INC(A2:A2001, 0.78)"?

    (a) The output is the percentile of the height of 78 inches.

    (b) The output is a height, the 78th percentile of the data set.

    (c) The output is a height, the 22nd percentile of the data set.

    (d) The output is a height, the third quartile of the data set.

2. Which of the following best explains the output of the function "=PERCENTRANK.INC(A2:A2001, 78)"?

    (a) The output is the percentile of the height of 78 inches.

    (b) The output is a height, the 78th percentile of the data set.

    (c) The output is a height, the 22nd percentile of the data set

    (d) The output is a height, the third quartile of the data set.

3. Which of the following best explains the output of the function "=QUARTILE.INC(A2:A2001,2)"?

    (a) The output is a percentile, specifically returning "0.50."

    (b) The output is a quartile number, specifically returning "2".

    (c) The output is a height, the median of the data set.

    (d) The output is a height which is greater than 2% of all heights in the data set.

4. Choose all of the following that explain the output of the function "=QUARTILE.INC(A2:A2001,4)"?

    (a) The output is a height, the maximum of the data set.

    (b) The output is a height, the 100th percentile of the data set.

    (c) The output is a height, the 4th quartile of the data set.

    (d) The output is a height, the 4th height when all heights are listed from smallest to largest.

5. The first and third quartiles for annual US family income in 2015 are $35,700 and $289,500, respectively. What percent of US families have an annual income between $35,700 and $289,500?

6. A friend who can bench press 275 pounds brags that he is exceptionally strong. In fact, he claims that he is in the 95th percentile for US males his age and weight. You search the internet and discover that the mean and standard deviation for the weight US males can bench press are 180 and 40 pounds, respectively. Do you believe your friend's claim? Read the options carefully and select the best answer.

    (a) Yes, because he can bench press 95 pounds (greater than 50%) more than the average US male.

    (b) No, because the US record is 570 pounds which is more than twice his best effort of 275 pounds.

    (c) Yes, because his press is more than 2 standard deviations above the mean.

    (d) No, because 95% of 180 is 171 so he would need to lift 351 pounds to be in the 95th percentile.

7. The poverty level is defined as the 20th percentile of annual family income. Currently the poverty level is $35,000. If the amount of variation in family income decreased but the mean remained the same, what would happen to the poverty level?

    (a) It would decrease to a value lower than $35,000

    (b) It would increase to a value greater than $35,000

    (c) Not enough information to answer the question

8. The monthly murder rate in a city (measured as homicides per 100,000 people) increased by 30% compared to one year previous. A local newspaper headline claimed: "Murder Rate Soaring!". As a person with knowledge of statistics, you decide to investigate further to see if the newspaper article is accurate or an exaggeration.
   Which of the following statistics would help you form your own opinion? Choose all that apply.

   (a) Mean annual murder rate for the past 10 years.

   (b) The population of the city.

   (c) The number of murders, by month, during the last year.

   (d) Mean of monthly murder rate for the past 10 years.

   (e) Standard deviation of the monthly murder rate for the last 10 years.

9. The mean IQ is 100 with a standard deviation of 15. Mensa is an exclusive organization that only accepts members who have an IQ in the top 2%. Unfortunately, Jeremy's IQ is just below the cutoff for membership.
   But recently is was determined that the standard deviation of IQ's is actually 12, not 15. The mean IQ remains 100 and Jeremy's IQ score didn't change either. Does this improve his chance to join Mensa?

   (a) No, because the mean has not changed.

   (b) No, because a smaller standard deviation means the cutoff for the top 2% will increase.

   (c) Yes, because a smaller standard deviation means there are fewer people with an IQ above Jeremy's.

   (d) Yes, because a smaller standard deviation means Jeremy's IQ score is closer to the mean.

   (e) No, because Jeremy's IQ did not change.

Exercises 10 – 11 use the Excel workbook MA101_ExtraPractice.xlsx.

10. The worksheet VS_RelativeStanding1_Prob&Sol contains 2000 heights and provides opportunity to practice finding percentiles, quartiles, standard deviations, etc.

11. The worksheet VS_RelativeStanding2_Prob&Sol contains the GDP per capita of all nations of the world in 2020, and provides opportunity to practice finding percentiles, quartiles, standard deviations, z-scores, etc.

Chapter 4

Making Decisions Using Probability

4.1 Probability

Contingency Tables

In 2014, two researchers conducted a study to determine the value of a certain type of polygraph test. Based on their study, they knew exactly half of the 100 subjects were innocent and the other half were guilty. Of the guilty subjects, 41 were caught through the polygraph test and labeled as deceptive, while three subjects from this group received an inconclusive result. Only 18 of the innocent subjects were found to be truthful with 5 inconclusive results for the innocent participants.

1. Complete the table below to display the results of this study, and list some observations you can determine from your table which would tell us about this study of the polygraph test.

	Deceptive	Inconclusive	Truthful	Total
Guilty				
Innocent				
Total				

Write down any observations you may have about this table.

-
-
-

This table is an example of a *contingency table* which gives frequency counts for the different categories, as well as row and column totals. The rows and columns are labeled with *categorical variables* to describe the data. Contingency tables are a powerful, and often intuitive, way of using probabilities.

Proportions and Percents

A *proportion* tells us how often an event occurs for the data set; for instance, we know that 5 of the 50 (or, 5/50) of the Innocent participants had tests marked as Inconclusive. We can use proportions like these to estimate the *probability* that such an event would happen in the *population*, not just in the *sample*. For a population we can use the proportion value to estimate the *probability* that event occurs. That is, the proportion 5/50 can be used to predict that 10% of Innocent people will have Inconclusive tests.

To practice these concepts, use your contingency table with the polygraph data to determine the following.

2. How many total participants were found to be deceptive?

3. What *proportion* of guilty participants was determined to be deceptive?

4. What *percent* of guilty participants was determined to be deceptive?

5. A guilty man takes this polygraph test. What is the probability he will be determined to be deceptive?

6. What *proportion* of deceptive participants were actually guilty?

7. What *percent* of deceptive participants were actually guilty?

8. A woman takes the test and is marked deceptive. What is the probability she is actually guilty?

9. Consider questions 5 and 8: if you were a police detective, which probability would be more important to you?

We consider the polygraph to have given a "correct result" provided that it identifies a guilty person as deceptive or an innocent person as truthful. We say that a result is "incorrect" if a guilty person is labeled as truthful (known as a false negative) or an innocent person as deceptive (known as a false positive).

10. What proportion of the tests gave a correct result?

11. What proportion of the tests gave an incorrect result?

12. Suppose you want 300 new participants to take the polygraph. Based on your data, how many people do you expect to receive a correct result?

*** Check in with your instructor.

Conditional Probabilities with Contingency Tables

Suppose you are inside and want to determine the probability that it will rain within the next hour. In most places, it rains less often than not, so you may judge the probability to be low. Now suppose you are told that it is currently very cloudy. Would this information about clouds change your probability that it will rain in the next hour? What if you were told it was very sunny, without any clouds outside? Would this change your probability of rain?

These are examples of *conditional probability*, where we take into consideration an event that has already occurred to help determine the probability of another event occurring.

We can write $P(\text{rain})$ to represent the probability it will rain. Sometimes it is easier to assign a letter to an event instead of writing out words. So we could say "Let A = it will rain in an hour." Then $P(A)$ represents the probability it will rain. To represent a conditional probability, we write

$$P(B|A) = \text{the probability of event } B \text{ occurring given the event } A \text{ has already occurred.}$$

Thus, in our example,

$$P(\text{rain}|\text{cloudy}) = \text{the probability that it will rain given that it is cloudy.}$$

We can determine conditional probabilities using contingency tables. To practice, we will return to the polygraph results.

	Deceptive	Inconclusive	Truthful	Total
Guilty	41	3	6	50
Innocent	27	5	18	50
Total	68	8	24	100

13. Imagine selecting a person at random from these 100 participants. Find the probability that the person selected is Guilty and Deceptive.

14. Now find the probability that a randomly selected person is Innocent and Deceptive.

15. Take your previous two answers, and add them together. What probability do you think you have found?

16. Use the table to find the probability that a person was Deceptive. How does this compare to the previous problem?

17. Now, find the probability that a person who is Guilty was determined to be Deceptive.

18. Find the probability that a person who is Innocent was determined to be Deceptive.

19. Take your previous two answers, and add them together. What happened?

We can take a closer look at a few of those problems.

20. The probability that a person who is Guilty was determined to be Deceptive is $\frac{41}{50}$.

   (a) This is a conditional probability. What was the event that had already occurred?

   (b) How many participants were both Guilty and Deceptive?.

   (c) How many participants were Guilty?

   (d) This problem begins by telling us that $P(\text{Deceptive} \mid \text{Guilty}) = \frac{41}{50}$. How can you use parts (b) and (c) to reach this conclusion?

   (e) Use the same procedure to calculate $P(\text{Truthful} \mid \text{Innocent})$.

21. The previous problem essentially states "Suppose you already know someone is Guilty. What is the probability they will test as Deceptive?" Of course, if you already know someone is Guilty, you probably wouldn't bother testing them. A more likely scenario is "A person just tested as Deceptive. What is the probability they are Guilty?" Find this probability; is this a conditional probability?

22. Using your own words, explain how to use a contingency table to find the probability that someone who is Guilty has a polygraph test marked Inconclusive. In your explanation, be sure to use the words "row" and "column" to help describe where to look to find the probabilities.

23. We use the "$\sim$" symbol to represent "not", or "anything other than". That is, $P(\sim\text{Deceptive})$ is the probability someone will be marked anything other than Deceptive (not necessarily Innocent).
   Find $P(\sim\text{Deceptive})$.

   *** **Check in with your instructor before moving to the next page.**

The COVID-19 pandemic brought to light many interesting questions involving probabilities, especially as pharmaceutical companies began testing their vaccines. Consider the data in the table below, released by Moderna, about COVID-19 infection rates of people who were given either the Moderna vaccine or a placebo.[1]

Moderna Covid Vaccine Clinical Trial	Contracted Covid (C)	Did not contract Covid ($\sim$C)	Total
Received Vaccine (V)	11	14,123	14,134
Received Placebo ($\sim$V)	185	13,888	14,073
Total	196	28,011	28,207

24. (a) How would you show that a vaccine was effective? What kind of evidence would you require before you agreed that a vaccine prevented a disease?

    (b) Does the table above lead you to think that the Moderna vaccine was effective at reducing the risk of contracting Covid?

    (c) Suppose you were convinced that your vaccine did reduce the chance of infection. How could you assign a number to "how good" your vaccine is? (Consider this: a vaccine that stops all infections could be considered 100% effective; a vaccine that didn't stop any infections would be 0% effective.)

25. What is, $P(C)$, the probability that someone from this population contracted Covid?

26. (a) What is the probability that someone who contracted Covid was vaccinated?

    (b) Write this probability as a conditional probability.

27. (a) What is the probability that someone who was vaccinated contracted Covid?

    (b) Write this probability as a conditional probability.

---

[1]See https://www.modernatx.com/covid19vaccine-eua/providers/clinical-trial-data.

28.   (a) What is the probability that someone who was given the placebo contracted Covid?

(b) Write this probability as a conditional probability.

29. Moderna claimed that its "vaccine efficacy" was 94.1%. With the eyes of the world on them, Moderna couldn't publicize this number without justification from the data.

(a) Using the percentages found above, show how Moderna arrived at its 94.1% figure.

(b) What is the meaning behind this calculation? That is, is this a reasonable way of determining the "efficacy" of a vaccine?

*** **Check in with your instructor before moving to the next page.**

The Apex, Baseline and Capstone companies all manufacture hiking boots. A local clothing goods store inspects the boots before selling them; if a pair is found to be Defective, it is returned to the manufacturer. The results of the past year's inspections are given below.

	Apex	Baseline	Capstone	Total
Good	875	152	285	1312
Defective	22	7	15	44
Totals	897	159	300	1356

Use this table to answer the following questions.

30. If a pair of boots is selected at random, what is the probability it is a Baseline boot?

31. Suppose a Good boot is selected; what is the probability it is a Capstone boot?

32. Write the above probability using proper conditional probability notation.

33. What is the probability that an Apex boot is Defective?

34. Write the above probability using proper conditional probability notation.

35. The shoe inspector grumbles "Apex boots are no good! Half of what I send back are Apex boots!"

    (a) There is an inherent conditional probability in that statement. Fill in the blanks to write out this probability.

    $$P(\underline{\hspace{3cm}}|\underline{\hspace{3cm}}) = 0.5 = 50\%.$$

    (b) While it is true that half the defective boots are Apex boots, this statement is also unfair. Why?

    (c) What probabilities are more important? Fill out the notation and give the probabilities.

    $$P(\underline{\hspace{2.5cm}}|\underline{\hspace{2.5cm}}) = \underline{\hspace{2.5cm}}.$$

    $$P(\underline{\hspace{2.5cm}}|\underline{\hspace{2.5cm}}) = \underline{\hspace{2.5cm}}.$$

    $$P(\underline{\hspace{2.5cm}}|\underline{\hspace{2.5cm}}) = \underline{\hspace{2.5cm}}.$$

36. The store is receiving a shipment of 40 Cornerstone boots. How many can we expect to be Defective?

*** **Check in with your instructor before moving to the next page.**

Review and Reflect

Take a moment to think back on this section. What were the main ideas? What did you find most interesting?

-

-

-

-

-

Probability Summary

- If A and B represent events (such as, flipping heads on a coin, or testing Innocent on a polygraph, etc.), then:

    - $P(A)$ represents the probability that event A will occur,

    - $P(\sim A)$ is the probability of "not A,", i.e., the probability that anything other than A will occur,

    - $P(A \text{ and } B)$ is the probability that both A and B will occur, and

    - $P(A \text{ or } B)$ is the probability that A or B will occur (i.e., that only A happens, or only B happens, or both A and B happen).

- All probabilities can be expressed as a number between 0 and 1. If $P(A) = 1$, the event will occur with certainty; if $P(A) = 0$, the event will not occur.

- A probability that incorporates the occurrence of another event is called a *conditional probability*. Given events A and B, the probability that B will occur, given that event A has occurred, is expressed $P(B|A)$.

- We have computed probabilities within the context of *contingency tables*, a table of data collected where the occurrence of different events, under different conditions, have been counted.

Exercises 4.1

Exercises 1 – 4 use the following table of 1800 test results for cancer.

	Positive Test (Pos)	Negative Test (Neg)	Total
Cancer (C)	4	1	5
No Cancer (∼C)	35	1760	1795
Total	39	1761	1800

1. Find $P(C)$ in decimal form.

2. What is the correct notation to express the probability that a patient whose test was positive actually has cancer?

    (a) $P(C)$

    (b) $P(\text{Pos}|C)$

    (c) $P(C|\text{Pos})$

    (d) $P(C \text{ and Pos})$

3. What is the probability that a patient whose test was positive actually has cancer?

    (a) 4/39 (about 10%)

    (b) 4/5 (80%)

    (c) 39/1761 (about 2%)

    (d) 39/1800 (about 2%)

4. What is the approximate number of false positives if 10,000 people took this test?

Exercises 5 – 9 use the following contingency table of favorite football teams of VMI cadets.

Favorite Team	VA	∼ VA	Total
Ravens	120	1	121
Other	20	65	85
Total	140	66	206

Let VA = event the Cadet is from Virginia and let R = event the Cadet is a Ravens fan.

5. Find $P(VA)$ in decimal form.

6. Find $P(\sim VA)$ in decimal form.

7. Find $P(VA \text{ or } \sim VA)$ in decimal form.

8. Find $P(VA \text{ or } \sim R)$ in decimal form.

9. Find $P(\sim VA \text{ and } R)$ in decimal form.

4.2 Sampling

In Class Activity: *BAT*tleship

White Nose Syndrome (WNS) is a disease of hibernating bats that has spread from the northeastern to the western United States, killing millions of bats since 2006. Currently biologists are trying to figure out how to stop the spread of WNS. Hence, it's important to be able to estimate populations of bats, which turns out to be a difficult task. Most bats are surveyed in caves while they are hibernating; however, some bats, like the eastern small-footed bat, hibernate in places where they are unlikely to be found. Due to this there is very little data on their population numbers.

COL Moosman of VMI's biology department has mentored cadets every summer since 2013 in collecting current data to try to extrapolate the total bat population on several *talus slopes* in the area. Their long-term goal is to be able to give the US Fish and Wildlife Service enough information to determine whether the eastern small-footed bat needs to be labeled as endangered.

Cadets who work with COL Moosman in the biology department actually go out into the field and look for bats on slopes. Since we are unable to take you out into the field to collect your own bat population data, each group will have a sample slope keeper. Their job is to provide the information about the number of bats on the slope while the other member determines where to take samples in order to extrapolate the total number of bats. If you are taking samples, select the proper number of boxes to sample by giving the sample slope keeper the row and column of the box you are interested in, kind of like the game *Battleship*.

Sample Slope 1

	A	B	C	D	E	F	G	H	I	J
1										
2										
3										
4										
5										
6										
7										
8										
9										
10										

1. Determine how many boxes there are in the slope. If you need to select 10% of the boxes, how many should you select?

2. Choose enough boxes to sample 10% of the boxes in the slope. For each box you choose, read its column letter (A through J) and its row (1 through 10) aloud to the slope keeper. The slope keeper will tell you how many bats are found in that part of the slope by looking at the slopes in Appendix D (on page 235). For example, if you ask about B3, then the slope keeper will tell you how many (if any) bats are in the box that is in the second column over and third row down. You may use the blank sample space above to keep track of how many bats you find in each box.

3. What selection method did you use to sample the slope? I.e., did you randomly choose squares, or did you cluster your sampling? Note: there is no correct answer. We just want to keep track of what you tried.

4. Make a prediction of how many bats you expect to see across this entire slope.

5. Using the same sample slope, take a sample of 25% of the area of the bat slope. Since you already have exposed 10% of the slope, how many more boxes can you search? Keep track of how many bats you find in each box.

6. Did you change your selection method, or did you keep it the same? Why?

7. Using the samples you took for sampling 25% of the area, make a prediction of how many bats are on the entire slope.

8. Have the slope keeper tell you how many bats there are in this slope. Calculate the percent error for both your estimations. Note that the percent error is given by the formula:

$$\%error = \frac{|predicted - actual|}{actual} * 100\%$$

9. Which sample was more accurate? Why might this be?

10. **Sample slope keeper: now switch to the SECOND sample slope.** Do one sample of 25% of the SECOND sample slope area. Be sure to keep track of how many bats are in each box.

Sample Slope 2

	A	B	C	D	E	F	G	H	I	J
1										
2										
3										
4										
5										
6										
7										
8										
9										
10										

11. Using only the information you just gathered, make a prediction of how many bats are on the slope.

12. Have the slope keeper tell you how many bats there are in this slope. Calculate the percent error of your prediction.

13. If your percent error was large, why do you think your answer was so far from the actual number of bats?

You might wonder why these two sample slopes are so different. The difference highlights something important about sampling: that it helps to understand some underlying assumptions about the population before we start our research. It turns out that these particular bats have different behaviors in different seasons. During most of the year, they are very spread out, like in the first slope; when cadets find an occupied crevice, it typically contains only one bat. However, the second slope represents an exaggeration of the mothering season, when it is not uncommon to find a larger crevice with one or more mothers and their pups, while the adult male bats are still typically alone.

Remember that COL Moosman is trying to determine the number of bats, but he and his cadet research assistants can't possibly search everywhere. By knowing whether it is mothering season or not, he can advise cadets to modify their search patterns. However, like any good researcher, he is open-minded to clever advice that has the potential to improve his work.

14. Brainstorm with your group to come up with two or three recommendations on how COL Moosman might actually improve his research as he aims to determine the local bat population. Your reporter should be prepared to share your group's ideas with the rest of the class.

We've started thinking about understanding a given population based on a small sample rather than the population itself. Two important factors to consider when sampling a population are sampling method and sample size. Ideally, we would like to take a completely random sample of our population in order to prevent bias in our data collection. Furthermore, taking a larger sample typically results in a more accurate prediction of the overall population. We will continue to explore these ideas in the context of polling and election results.

Sampling Mini-Summary

- It can be hard to sample a population when you know nothing about the underlying *distribution* of the population.

- Unless specific information about a population's distribution is known, the best method of sampling is to take a *random sample*. That is, choose from the population without bias or reason.

*** **Check in with your instructor.**

Part 2: Predicting Elections: Estimating Population Proportion

The 2016 Presidential Election campaign was very unusual compared to previous election cycles for a number of reasons. Two events that took place that year are of particular interest to statisticians. First, Secretary Clinton was expected to win the Michigan Democratic Primary by a large margin, with polls showing her leading Senator Sanders by 21 percentage points (i.e, polls showed that roughly 60% of voters would vote for Clinton, vs. about 40% for Sanders). Instead, Sanders won narrowly, with less than a 51/49 percentage split.

The second event of interest is the actual presidential election. Because of the Electoral College, one cannot simply look at one poll and make a prediction of the outcome. Rather, one must make predictions about each state and aggregate that information with the number of votes each state has within the college. The overwhelming majority of reputable media outlets forecast a high likelihood that Secretary Clinton would win the election: Nate Silver's 538 website predicted Clinton had a 71% chance of winning; the New York Times gave her a 84% chance of winning, and the Princeton Election Consortium predicted her winning chances to be at least 95%. However, the actual election turned out far differently from these forecasts, with businessman Donald Trump losing the popular vote but winning the election by taking most of the hard-to-call "tossup" states and even some states many predicted would vote for Clinton.

All of the predictions cited above relied on polling data. Because of a number of limitations, only a *sample* of voters were asked, prior to the election, for whom they intended to vote. Sampling provides a method of making a prediction, which inherently runs a risk of being incorrect. The above reputable media sources acknowledged these risks, citing probabilities that Clinton (and, likewise, Trump) would win. We should not conclude that the 538 website "got it wrong." They predicted that Trump had a chance of winning, albeit a smaller chance of winning than Clinton.

Polling random samples is a highly effective method for measuring a characteristic of a population. This section will investigate some of the principles involved, including the principles behind how the above percentages were generated.

There are three main characteristics of a population that are often measured through random samples. We are concerned here with measuring *population proportion*. In elections, we want to measure "What proportion of the population will vote for Clinton?" Polling is not limited to elections, nor people, though. For instance, a farmer may take a random sample of his orange crop to estimate what proportion of his oranges is below a certain size, and a manufacturer may take a random sample of its product to see what proportion is defective. The other characteristics that are often measured are the *population mean* and *population standard deviation*. The orange farmer may want to approximate the average weight of his oranges (the mean weight), and know how those weights are distributed (the standard deviation of the weights).

Statisticians use a lowercase n to describe the number of people/things sampled, and use an uppercase N to describe the size of the total population. If 50 students are sampled from a school of 2500 students, we would have $n = 50$ and $N = 2500$.

Simulating Elections

We explore the process of random sampling by simulating a small town election between two candidates, Adams and Banks. In this small town, about 55% of the population support Adams over Banks, though not everyone in the town will vote (so Banks has a chance of winning).

The workbook MtM_Unit3a_CourseContent.xlsx contains several worksheets that simulate possible elections and the sampling of some of the voters. We are interested in how often the predicted winner of the sample is the same as the true winner of the election.

Throughout this activity, we will be updating our worksheets with the F9 key in order to run multiple simulations. (Computers vary in how the F9 key is accessed. On some, just press that key; on others one might need to press fn + F9 or command + F9.) This action will be referred to as **refreshing the worksheet**.

Experiment 1

15. Open the workbook MtM_Unit3a_CourseContent.xlsx and look at the tab named SA_PredictElections1. This sheet simulates 100 people voting ($N = 100$), with 10 people being polled before the vote ($n = 10$). The voters are randomly generated; each time the worksheet is refreshed or any data is entered into a cell, a new election is simulated.

   - In cell D2 the winner of the election is given. Since there are 100 voters, the candidate with 51 or more votes is declared the winner. It is not uncommon in this scenario for Adams and Banks to tie with 50 votes each; in such a case, D2 will display "Tie!".

   - In cell F2 the predicted winner, based on the 10-person poll, is given, i.e., the person who received 6 or more votes from the poll. As with the actual election, for the poll , it is possible to predict a tie.

16. Refresh the worksheet enough times to see Adams and Banks each win the overall election once, as well as see the election end in a tie.

17. We want to estimate how often the predicted winner actually wins the election. Refresh the worksheet 20 times to see the outcome of 20 elections. Record "Yes" if the predicted and actual outcomes are both "Adams", both "Banks" or both "Tie!", otherwise record "No". Record the results of each election in Table 4.1 below.

Table 4.1: Simulating 20 Elections with $n = 10$, $N = 100$

Iteration	Correct Prediction (Yes/No)	Iteration	Correct Prediction (Yes/No)
1		11	
2		12	
3		13	
4		14	
5		15	
6		16	
7		17	
8		18	
9		19	
10		20	

18. Record the number of times, out of 20, that the predicted outcome matched the actual outcome.

19. Using your answer from above, give the percentage of times the poll correctly predicted the outcome.

Experiment 2

In Experiment 1, we used the power of a spreadsheet to simulate an election. However, we still did manual work: to record the results of 20 elections, we pressed F9 20 times and recorded each outcome individually. We now simulate even more elections, letting Excel do all the work for us.

20. Open the workbook MtM_Unit3a_CourseContent.xlsx and look at the tab named SA_PredictElections2. Columns C through GT of this sheet each simulate 100 people voting ($N = 100$), with 10 people being polled before the vote ($n = 10$). The voters are randomly generated; each time the worksheet is refreshed or any data is entered into a cell, a new election is simulated. So by refreshing the worksheet once, we can simulate 200 elections! Cell A2 gives the number of times the prediction matched the actual election outcome.

- Row 2 contains the predicted winner based on the 10-person poll for that election, i.e. the person who received 6 or more votes from the poll. It is not uncommon in this scenario for Adams and Banks to tie the poll with 5 votes each; in such a case, the entry in Row 2 will display "Tie!".

- Row 3 contains the actual outcome of the election. Since there are 100 voters in each election, the candidate with 51 or more votes is declared the winner. Much like with the predicted outcome, it is possible to have a tie as a result.

21. Refresh the worksheet enough times to see Adams and Banks each win the election in column C once, as well as see the election end in a tie.

22. After completing the task in #21, press F9 one more time. Record the number of correctly predicted elections here.

23. In the previous problem, you simulated a total of 200 elections. What percentage of the time did the predicted and actual outcomes agree?

Experiment 3

24. Open the workbook MtM_Unit3a_CourseContent.xlsx and look at the tab named SA_PredictElections3. Columns C through GT of this sheet each simulate 20 people voting ($N = 20$), with 10 people being polled before the vote ($n = 10$). As before, the voters are randomly generated; each time the worksheet is refreshed or any data is entered into a cell, a new election is simulated and by refreshing the worksheet once, we can simulate 200 elections. Cell A2 gives the number of times the prediction matched the actual election outcome.

- Row 2 contains the predicted winner based on the 10-person poll for that election, i.e. the person who received 6 or more votes from the poll. It is not uncommon in this scenario for Adams and Banks to tie the poll with 5 votes each; in such a case, the entry in Row 2 will display "Tie!".

- Row 3 contains the actual outcome of the election. Since there are 20 voters in each election, the candidate with 11 or more votes is declared the winner. Much like with the predicted outcome, it is possible to have a tie as a result.

25. Refresh the worksheet enough times to see Adams and Banks each win the election in column C once, as well as see the election end in a tie.

26. After completing the task in #25, press F9 one more time. Record the number of correctly predicted elections here.

27. In the previous problem, you simulated a total of 200 elections. What percentage of the time did the polls predict the actual outcome of the election?

One may be surprised at how many times the poll-based prediction was incorrect. One might think that the accuracy of a poll is increased by polling a higher percentage of the population. That statement is only partially true, and it doesn't fully reveal the principles involved when choosing the number of people to poll. We will explore this further in a later class discussion.

Now it is time to compare the results of your simulations to the rest of the class. Fill in your answers from the predicting elections simulation result table that your group filled out for homework. Once everyone in the class has written their down results, complete Table 4.2 and compare your results with that of your peers.

Table 4.2: Predicting Elections Simulation Results

	Percentage of Correctly Predicted Elections $N = 100, n = 10$, 20 simulations	Percentage of Correctly Predicted Elections $N = 100, n = 10$, 200 simulations	Percentage of Correctly Predicted Elections $N = 20, n = 10$, 200 simulations
Group 1			
Group 2			
Group 3			
Group 4			
Group 5			
Group 6			
Group 7			
Group 8			

Do you notice any patterns?

Part 3: Simulating Larger Elections

It is common to see fine print on political polling results that says something like *"Margin of error ±3%."* In this next set of experiments, we'll delve a little into how this margin of error can be determined.

Open MtM_Unit3a_CourseContent.xlsx and look at the tab named SA_ElecAcc1. This worksheet simulates 100 elections with 500 voters, wherein 50 were polled. In Row 2, the winner of the poll is given, whereas in Row 3, the actual election winner is given. In Row 6, the percentage of those polled who support Adams is given, and in Row 7 the percentage of all voters who support Adams is given. In Row 8, the difference of these two percentages is calculated.

Experiment 1

28. After opening the SA_ElecAcc1 tab, refresh the spreadsheet <u>once</u>. Answer the following without pressing any other keys.

    (a) What percentage of the population did you sample?

    (b) How many times did the sample percentage of Adams support **exactly match** the population percentage of Adams support? (See cell A7.)

    (c) What was the biggest difference in the sample and population percentages? (See cell A11.)

    (d) Look in cell A11; what command is used to find the biggest difference?

    (e) How many times did the sample accurately predict the outcome of the election?

    (f) How many times was the sample percentage *within* 5% of the population percentage? (See cell A15.)

Experiment 2

29. Now open the SA_ElectAcc2 tab. Here 100 elections are simulated where 100 voters are polled from a population of 1,000. Answer the following without pressing any other keys.

    (a) What percentage of the population did you sample?

(b) How many times did the sample percentage of Adams support **exactly match** the population percentage of Adams support?

(c) What was the biggest difference in the sample and population percentages?

(d) How many times did the sample accurately predict the outcome of the election?

(e) How many times was the sample percentage *within* 5% of the population proportion?

Experiment 3

30. Now open the SA_ElectAcc3 tab. Here 100 elections are simulated where 100 voters are polled from a population of 10,000.

    (a) If there are 100 columns of simulated elections, and in each, there are 10,000 voters, how many simulated voters are represented on this worksheet?

    (b) Press F9 once. How long did it take your computer to update this number of simulated voters?

31. Answer the following without pressing any other keys.

    (a) What percentage of the population did you sample?

    (b) How many times did the sample percentage of Adams support **exactly match** the population percentage of Adams support?

    (c) What was the biggest difference in the sample and population percentages?

    (d) How many times did the sample accurately predict the outcome of the election?

    (e) How many times was the sample percentage *within* 5% of the population proportion?

*** **Check in with your instructor.**

Review and Reflect

Take a moment to think back on this section. What were the main ideas? What did you find most interesting?

-

-

-

-

-

Elections Summary

We ran a lot of different simulations yet haven't made any concrete discoveries nor conclusions. There are a few take-aways you should be aware of, though.

- Spreadsheets like Excel are extremely useful in helping us understand random events. (Excel was easily able to simulate the actions of 1,000,000 voters!)

- *Sampling* is the process by which only some parts of a population are measured. We sample in hopes of understanding the full population.

- Sampling is not exact. We will learn soon how to best interpret our sampling results.

- We sample, instead of polling everyone, because:

    - polling everyone takes too much time,

    - polling everyone takes too much money, and

    - polling everyone is, in general, hard.

- If a poll predicts a candidate has a 25% chance of winning, and that candidate does indeed win, we cannot conclude "the poll got it wrong." The poll predicted the candidate *had a chance*.

- Sampling accurately depends on understanding the underlying distribution. Sampling bats on a talus slope is hard if you do not understand how bats gather.

Exercises 4.2

Suppose 100 people are asked "Do you prefer Pepsi or Coke?" and 53 respond "Pepsi." Use this scenario to answer the questions in Exercises 1 – 3.

1. What proportion of the sample preferred Pepsi over Coke?

2. How many people would therefore prefer Pepsi out of a population of 2,500?

3. If you were told the margin of error was 10% what would the range be of people who prefer Pepsi?

4. After the Michigan Democratic Primary results, it was discovered that much of the polling was based on telephone interviews made to landlines. Why would this lead to inaccurate polling results?

4.3 Confidence Intervals for Proportions

We ended Section 4.2 with running election simulations with different numbers of voters (N), and different numbers of people being sampled (n). We looked at how often the predicted voting percentage for Adams was within 5% of the actual voting percentage (which is different than asking if we correctly predicted who won).

Fill in the results of your simulation in a row below, and if possible, fill in rows with the results of other students/groups.

Predicting Elections Simulation Results within 5% of the Population Proportion

	Number of times within 5% of population proportion		
	$N = 500, n = 50$	$N = 1000,$ $n = 100$	$N = 10,000,$ $n = 100$
Group 1			
Group 2			
Group 3			
Group 4			
Group 5			
Group 6			
Group 7			
Group 8			
Totals			
Total number of simulations run in each column:			

Do you notice any patterns?

For the rest of this unit, we will use the Excel worksheet Statistics Calculator.xlsx to calculate *confidence intervals* and perform *hypothesis tests* (we'll soon learn what these terms mean). You will need to have this on your computer to be able to complete the lecture notes, homework assignments, and Canvas quizzes.

Statisticians generally let p represent the total population proportion of some trait; in our election scenario above, the proportion of the population that supported Adams was supposed to be $p = 0.55$. In real life, we don't know p, so we try to estimate it by finding the proportion of that trait in our random sample. We call the proportion of the random sample $\hat{p}$. Hopefully $\hat{p} \approx p$, where "$\approx$" means "approximately equal".

Look back at Experiments #2 and #3 (i.e., the 2nd and 3rd columns in the table above). In each, the sample proportion should have been within 5% of the population proportion about 70% of the time. Using the p and $\hat{p}$ notation, we can rephrase this as "When sampling 100 people and $\hat{p}$ is approximately 0.55 (i.e., 55%), then about 70% of the time the true population proportion is between 50% and 60%." That is, p is between $\hat{p} - 0.05$ and $\hat{p} + 0.05$, which we can also write as "$\hat{p} - 0.05 < p < \hat{p} + 0.05$", i.e, "$0.5 < p < 0.6$." **Did we see this in our results?**

The Basic Principles of Confidence Intervals

If we were to take a random sample of 100 voters and found 55% supported Adams, we have "confidence" that 70% of the time the true proportion of Adams supporters is between 50% and 60%. That means, of course, that 30% of the time we expect the true proportion to be outside of that range, and hence we could potentially incorrectly predict an election if we are not careful. An interval like $(0.5, 0.6)$ that contains the true population proportion 70% of the time is called a *70% confidence interval*. The associated *error* in this example is $E = 0.05$, or $E = 5\%$.

The principle concepts of confidence intervals can be visualized with the worksheet CI_Visualizing_Conf._Int., in the Excel workbook MtM_Unit3b_CourseContent.xlsx. Opening this sheet shows more simulated elections between Adams and Banks, though under different circumstances. Key things to note:

- In Column B, in rows 20-24, you will see the % that supports Adams in a population of 1000 voters. This percentage changes each time F9 is pressed.

- Columns C through L show the results of 10 different polls, each sampling 50 voters.

- Each of these 10 polls predicts a proportion of support for Adams. Using that level of support, we can construct an 80% confidence interval around that proportion. (We haven't yet learned how to compute that interval; the spreadsheet will do it for us right now.)

- Now look at the graph at the top of the worksheet.

  - The dashed, vertical line represents the true proportion of support for Adams. (This changes each time you press F9.)

  - The 80% confidence interval for each sample is constructed and graphed, represented by short line segments. If the endpoints of the line segments are on opposite sides of the dashed line, then the confidence interval actually contains the population proportion.

  - Press F9 repeatedly, each time counting how many intervals do not contain the population proportion.

  - You should find that, on average, 2 confidence intervals do not contain the dashed line. That is, about 80% of the confidence intervals *do* contain the population proportion.

  - Because 80% of the constructed intervals actually contain the population proportion, we call these intervals "80% confidence intervals."

An important take-away is what we have confidence in: *the process*. We have created a process that, 80% of the time, creates an interval that captures the population proportion. If an interval is created, we *can't* say "There's an 80% chance the population proportion is in that interval." In reality, the population proportion either is, or isn't, in that interval; chance no longer applies. Since we don't know if that particular interval does contain the population proportion, we can instead say "We have 80% confidence that that interval contains the population proportion." We have confidence in the process, and don't make statements about probabilities. (It's a nuanced issue that takes time to become accustomed to.)

1. The phrase "70% confident" in the context of a 70% confidence interval for a population proportion p means: (choose all that apply)

    (a) 70% of similarly constructed intervals would contain the value of the population proportion.

    (b) we are 70% confident that the interval actually contains the value of the population proportion.

    (c) the probability that the sample proportion falls in the calculated interval is 0.70.

    (d) we are 70% confident that the sample proportion is equal to the population proportion

2. Earlier we created the 70% confidence interval $(0.5, 0.6)$ in the context of an Adams/Banks election. What if we wanted to be more confident about our interval that is supposed to contain p? If we wanted to be 95% confident that our interval contained p, for instance, should we make our interval bigger or smaller than 0.5 to 0.6? In other words, would a 95% confidence interval be wider or more narrow than a 70% confidence interval?

We can think of a confidence interval as a "net" that is thrown to catch something. To be more confident that we'll catch our prey, we should use a wider net. Therefore, a 95% confidence interval will be *bigger* than a 70% confidence interval: to be more sure we capture the true population percentage, we use a wider interval.

Establishing Confidence Intervals

Most of the time confidence intervals are formed with higher than 70% confidence. It is common to see 90%, 95% and 99% confidence intervals in use. There is a relatively simple formula for creating these intervals. You won't be expected to memorize this formula, but it is shown so you can understand what factors are important. The necessary notation:

$$p = \text{population proportion (unknown)}$$
$$\hat{p} = \text{sample proportion}$$
$$n = \text{sample size}$$
$$z = z \text{ score; useful values are given in Table 4.3 below}$$
$$E = \text{margin of error}$$

Let $E = z\sqrt{\dfrac{\hat{p}(1-\hat{p})}{n}}$. The confidence interval corresponding to z is $(\hat{p} - E, \hat{p} + E)$, also written as $\hat{p} \pm E$ or $\hat{p} - E < p < \hat{p} + E$.

Table 4.3: Useful z-scores

Confidence Level	z
70%	1.036
80%	1.281
90%	1.645
95%	1.96
99%	2.576

3. Consider our scenario from before: we have sampled 100 people and have found 55% support Adams. Let's construct the 70% confidence interval for the population proportion that favors Adams.

   Using the chart above, we have $z = 1.036$. Our sample proportion is $\hat{p} = 0.55$, and we have sampled 100 people, so $n = 100$. Putting this together, we find

   $$E = z\sqrt{\frac{\hat{p}(1-\hat{p})}{n}} = 1.036\sqrt{\frac{0.55 * 0.45}{100}} = 0.052.$$

   (Note: Perform this calculation in Excel. Excel (and most other spreadsheets) use sqrt() for the square-root command; =sqrt(16) will return 4.)

   Thus the 70%-confidence interval is

   $$(0.55 - 0.052, 0.55 + 0.052) = (0.498, 0.602),$$

   which is close to the $(0.5, 0.6)$ interval we described before.

4. Look at the z-scores from Table 4.3. As the confidence level increases, do the z-values increase or decrease?

5. Consider again the formula for error: $E = z\sqrt{\frac{\hat{p}(1-\hat{p})}{n}}$.

   (a) If the confidence level increases, does the error increase or decrease?

   (b) To reduce the margin of error in a confidence interval for a population parameter p, which of the following should be done?

      i. decrease the sample size n.
      ii. increase the sample size n.
      iii. conduct a biased survey.
      iv. increase the confidence level.

6. **IMPORTANT:** In the formula for the margin of error, E, we need to know the sample proportion $\hat{p}$, the sample size n, and a z-score. What quantity is missing that one might think would be important? (As a hint: think about our simulation of the Adams and Banks election.)

Open the Excel workbook Statistics Calculator.xlsx and select the tab for "Conf. Interval Proportion". Use the Excel sheet to help determine the following.

7. Suppose 100 people are randomly sampled and $\hat{p} = 0.55$, as in part of our Adams/Banks election example.

   (a) At the 70% confidence level, use the calculator to find the margin of error E. (Your answer should match what you found in question #3.)

   (b) Use your result from part (a) to construct the associated 70% confidence interval (look to see where the Statistics Calculator displays that information for you).

   (c) Explain your results from part (b) in the context of the Adams/Banks election scenario. What does your confidence interval mean in words?

8. Suppose you wanted to be 95% sure that your interval contained p, the true proportion of Adams supporters.

    (a) Find the 95% confidence interval. (Again, $\hat{p} = 0.55$ and $n = 100$.)

    (b) Is E bigger/smaller than in problem 7?

    (c) Is the confidence interval bigger/small than in question #7?

9. Suppose 1000 people are randomly sampled and again we find the proportion of Adams supporters is 55%.

    (a) Find the 95% confidence interval.

    (b) Is E bigger/smaller than in problem 8?

    (c) Is the confidence interval bigger/small than in problem 8?

10. Suppose only 20 people are polled. Find the error E associated with the 90% confidence interval, assuming that $\hat{p} = 0.55$. Does your answer imply that polling 20 people will produce useful results?

11. Suppose 1000 residents of Roanoke, VA are polled by selecting names, at random, out of the phone book. They are asked "Are you retired?" Suppose 64% respond "Yes."

    (a) Construct the 99% confidence interval for p, the proportion of retired residents of Roanoke.

    (b) On a practical level, what is wrong with the above sampling method? Even though residents are stated to be chosen at random, why might the results not give an accurate representation of the Roanoke population?

*** Check in with your instructor before moving on.

Determining Sample Size

Our formula for error, E, requires that we know z, $\hat{p}$ and n. It is not uncommon to desire a certain confidence level (say 95%) and have a preference for the size of E (for example, we may want $E = 0.02$ or 2%). In such situations, we need to find the sample size n that provides this error value at the given confidence level. For instance, a manufacturing company wants to determine what proportion of its product is defective, and they may determine they want their results to be accurate to $\pm 1\%$ at the 99% confidence level. The quality control manager must determine the size of the random sample to test.

12. Starting with $E = z\sqrt{\dfrac{\hat{p}(1-\hat{p})}{n}}$, solve for n.

Your answer contains the product $\hat{p}(1-\hat{p})$. Since we have not yet sampled anything, we do not know what $\hat{p}$ is. The value $\hat{p} = 0.5$ will result in the most error and ensures that the calculated n will be large enough, even in the worst-case scenario. The Excel workbook Statistics Calculator.xlsx will also be able to calculate the sample size. Use columns **E** and **F** on the "Conf. Interval Proportion" tab.

13. Hopefully you were able to come up with the equation $n = z^2\dfrac{\hat{p}(1-\hat{p})}{E^2}$. Using this equation, determine the sample size n that gives an error of $E = 0.01$ at the 99% confidence level where $\hat{p}$ is not known.

14. The previous result should return a rather large number for n. In hopes of significantly reducing the sample size, the quality control manager decides that a 3% margin of error would be okay, though still at the 99% confidence level.

    (a) Determine the sample size that gives an error of $E = 0.03$ at the 99% confidence level.

    (b) How much bigger was your first n value compared to the second?

15. The quality control manager realizes the formula is a worst case formula. While a formal sample has not been taken, the manager believes that no more than 1% of the product is defective. Letting $\hat{p} = 0.01$, use the equation for error found in Question 12 to determine the sample size for a 99% confidence level, and $E = \pm 3\%$.

Some Additional Information

Random sampling is rarely used to determine an exact (or, nearly exact) proportion. Rather, it is used to get a good enough approximation of the true value. The previous three questions show that to get a highly accurate approximation (99% confidence with an error of $\pm 1\%$), without any prior knowledge about the population proportion, the sample size needs to be over 15,000. This is a rather large number; it can be difficult to obtain a sample of this size in some contexts. The quality control manager might have high hopes of very accurately determining the defective rate, only to have to change expectations. By increasing the acceptable amount of possible error from 1% to 3%, and by making a reasonable guess about the true value of p, the sample size can be significantly reduced.

Suppose that in an election, random sampling shows support for Adams to be at 60%, with an error of $\pm 5\%$ at the 95% confidence level. This recognizes a 5% chance that the true support for Adams is outside of the interval $(0.55, 0.65)$, but even then, the likelihood that the level of Adams support is *under* 50% is probably very low. This gives greater confidence in predicting that Adams will win the election. In this situation, a highly accurate estimate of Adams support isn't needed (such as, 59% vs. 60%); we just need to be reasonably confident that the level of Adams support is above 50%.

All of the above is predicated on a number of important requirements.

- The sample must be a true random sample. In practice, it can be hard to obtain a true random sample. Picking a random sample from voter registration rosters is rather straightforward. Determining if these individuals are actually likely to vote is difficult, as is actually getting a response from the people you have randomly selected. Each field that relies on selecting random samples from a population has accepted methods of dealing with the difficulty of finding a truly random sample. (In engineering, random samples are often items from an assembly line, and it may be a simple matter to select items. In political science, the difficulties listed above are well known and practices of dealing with these difficulties are just as well known.)

- Each *trial* (i.e., polling a person or testing whether an item is defective, etc.) must be independent of the other trials. If Person A supports Adams in a poll, this should not increase/decrease the likelihood that Person B supports Adams. (So polls taken by a show of hands can generate unreliable results. If it seems as though a lot of people support a certain candidate, others may be unlikely to show their dissent.)

- In the sample, there must be at least 5 of each outcome. In terms of our election, we need to have at least 5 preferring Adams and 5 preferring Banks. (This requirement is rooted in something called the Central Limit Theorem, an important theorem in statistics.)

Review and Reflect

Take a moment to think back on this section. What were the main ideas? What did you find most interesting?

-
-
-
-
-

Proportion Confidence Interval Summary

- If a population's proportion p needs to be approximated, one can take a random sample and measure the sample's proportion $\hat{p}$.

- The sample proportion $\hat{p}$ is our best estimate of the value of p. To get a better idea of how good this estimate is, we can construct a confidence interval.

- The two main factors influencing the size of the confidence interval (determined by its error E) are:

    - The sample size n: increasing n decreases E, and
    - The confidence level: increasing the confidence level increases E.

- Perhaps surprisingly, the size of the population N does not effect the error E. In other words, we need not try to sample a certain *percentage* of the population to get a good sample. We just need to sample a good *number* n.

- We have a certain level of *confidence* in a confidence interval that is based on our confidence in the *process* of making confidence intervals.

    - Given a 90% confidence interval, we have 90% confidence that the interval contains the true proportion.
    - We know that 90% of the 90% confidence intervals for a proportion actually contain the true population proportion.

- To decrease the size of a confidence interval, we can

    - increase the sample size, or
    - decrease the confidence level.

Exercises 4.3

In Exercises 1 – 4, fill in the blank with either the word "increase" or "decrease".

1. Increasing the confidence level will _____ the size of the confidence interval.

2. Increasing the sample size n will _____ the size of the confidence interval.

3. To decrease the size of a confidence interval, one can _____ the confidence level.

4. To decrease the size of a confidence interval, one can _____ the sample size.

Exercises 5 – 12 use Statistics Calculator.xlsx, **although some problems may not require the spreadsheet explicitly.**

5. Thirty students were weighed from an elementary school of 457 students. Eleven were found to be overweight.

    (a) What is the value for the sample proportion?

    (b) Give the 90% confidence interval for the proportion of students in the elementary school who are overweight.

    (c) The 99% confidence interval for the proportion of students in the elementary school who are overweight was determined to be (0.14, 0.59). What range of the number of students does this interval correspond to?

6. An email is sent out to the 1700 members of the VMI Corps asking "Do you plan on commissioning upon graduation?" 150 cadets respond, with 110 indicating "Yes." (This scenario is hypothetical.)

    (a) What is the sample size?

    (b) Are the results likely to be reliable?

    (c) Suppose 150 cadets are selected at random, and 110 report intentions to commission.

        i. What is the margin of error for the 95% confidence interval for the true proportion of cadets who intend to commission.

        ii. Give the 95% confidence interval of the true proportion of cadets who intend to commission.

7. On April 11 and 12 of 2017, Ipsos conducted a poll, on behalf of National Public Radio, related to issues of tax policy. Of the 1,010 Americans polled, 55% agreed to the statement "Federal income taxes should be cut for all income levels." Assuming that the pollsters randomly selected their sample, can one reasonably conclude "Over half of Americans believe federal income taxes should be cut for all income levels"? Choose all that apply.

    (a) Yes, at the 90% confidence level.

    (b) Yes, at the 95% confidence level.

    (c) Yes, at the 99% confidence level.

8. An ICR Research Group study reported that 70% of 1002 people sampled claimed to have voted in a recent presidential election. Find the 99% confidence interval for the proportion of the population who voted in the election.

9. Assume the VMI Corps consists of exactly 1700 cadets. Cadets are to be randomly sampled in order to determine the proportion of the Corps that shares a characteristic (male, Democrat, green–eyed, voted, donates blood, owns a gun, watches soccer, enjoys math, etc.).

    (a) How many cadets should be randomly sampled so the error is within 4%, at the 95% confidence level?

    (b) How many cadets should be randomly sampled so the error, at the 90% confidence level, is within ± 50 cadets?

10. Suppose that at the end of an academic year, 317 VMI cadets graduate and 173 commission. What proportion, p, of VMI cadets commission in this scenario?

11. Suppose that at the end of an academic year, 317 VMI cadets graduate and 173 commission. Should a confidence interval for the proportion, p, of VMI cadets who commission be constructed?

    (a) Yes, it is important to estimate how many cadets commission.

    (b) No, this is a population proportion and not a sample. We do not need to use an estimate.

    (c) Yes, the interval at the 90% confidence level between 50% and 59% of cadets commission.

    (d) No, a majority of cadets do not commission. The interval at the 95% confidence level between 49% and 60% of cadets commission.

12. In a randomized controlled trial, insecticide-treated bed nets were tested as an easy to reduce malaria. Among 344 infants using these bed nets, 19 developed malaria. Among 255 infants not using these bed nets, 25 developed malaria.

    (a) Construct the 95% confidence interval for the proportion of infants who contracted malaria while using treated bed nets.

    (b) Construct the 95% confidence interval for the proportion of infants who contracted malaria while not using treated bed nets.

    (c) The claim states that infants using treated bed nets have a lower incidence of malaria. Is this claim supported through your confidence interval results? Defend your answer.

4.4 Confidence Intervals for Means

We will continue to use the Excel worksheet Statistics Calculator.xlsx to calculate confidence intervals. You will also need the Excel workbook MtM_Unit3b_CourseContent.xlsx.

Introduction to Confidence Intervals for Means

We have studied the use of random sampling to approximate a population proportion. Our main context was one of sampling a population of voters to predict the outcome of an election. Key to our study was the concept of the *confidence interval*. While our best approximation of the population proportion p is $\hat{p}$, the proportion of the sample, we are also pretty sure that they are not exactly equal. Our previous work showed how to compute a margin of error E where we could be, for instance, "95% confident that the true population proportion p is within $\pm E$ of $\hat{p}$."

We now consider approximating the population mean, and our methodology is similar to that of estimating population proportions. We will use the mean $\bar{x}$ of a random sample to approximate the population mean μ. We will also generate a margin of error E that will enable us to say, for instance, "We are 95% confident that the population mean μ is within $\pm E$ of $\bar{x}$."

Here are some initial questions that will help us understand the margin of error E.

1. Suppose you sample 20 people from a population and find the mean age of those sampled is 50. Answer yes or no to each of the following questions.

    (a) Would you be surprised to find out that the population mean is 51? (Y/N)

    (b) Would you be surprised to find out that the population mean is 45? (Y/N)

    (c) Would you be surprised to find out that the population mean is 60? (Y/N)

    (d) Would you be surprised to find out that the population mean is 30? (Y/N)

2. Suppose you sample 1,000 people from a population and find the mean age of those sampled is 50. Answer yes or no to each of the following questions.

    (a) Would you be surprised to find out that the population mean is 51? (Y/N)

    (b) Would you be surprised to find out that the population mean is 45? (Y/N)

    (c) Would you be surprised to find out that the population mean is 60? (Y/N)

    (d) Would you be surprised to find out that the population mean is 30? (Y/N)

Our previous experience tells us that our best guess of the mean age is 50, but we don't expect the mean age to be exactly 50. When sampling 20 people, we are probably not surprised to find the true mean is actually 51, though finding the true mean is actually 30 would be surprising. You may/may not find true means of 45 or 60 surprising.

When sampling 1,000 people, we expect our sample mean age to be a more accurate approximation than when we sampled just 20. We would not expect the true mean to be 30 or 60; one may even be surprised to find the true mean is 51.

Mini-conclusion #1:

We expect our computation of the margin of error E to take into account the number n of items/people sampled. When n is large, we expect E to be small. (We discovered the same result with proportion confidence intervals.)

3. Consider the two lists of numbers below. Each has a mean of about 50. Consider each as being a random sample from two different populations.

Sample from Population #1:	91	50	40	44	57	66	42	35	90	55
	44	51	49	56	43	53	41	45	48	6

Sample from Population #2:	49	51	50	51	48	50	50	51	49	50
	49	50	49	51	51	49	50	51	51	51

Are you more confident that Population #1 or Population #2 truly has a mean close to 50? Why?

The sample from Population #1 has values ranging from 6 up to 90 and 91, whereas the sample from Population #2 only contains the values 48, 49, 50 and 51. We likely have more confidence that Population #2 has a true mean close to 50 than Population #1.

Mini-conclusion #2:

We expect our computation of the margin of error E to take into account the spread of the data in the sample. If the spread is large we expect E to be large. The measure of spread that we'll use is the standard deviation, s, of the sample.

Computing Confidence Intervals

Given a sample mean $\bar{x}$, we want to determine E and the confidence interval that will allow us to say "We are 95% confident that the true population mean μ is between $\bar{x} - E$ and $\bar{x} + E$; that is, μ is in $(\bar{x} - E, \bar{x} + E)$."

The formula for E looks straightforward, and includes the two values we expected from our mini-conclusions before:

$$E = t\frac{s}{\sqrt{n}},$$

where s is the sample standard deviation, n is the size of the sample, and t is a critical value from the "Student t-distribution." As before, we won't need to memorize this formula, but we do want to understand the factors involved.

The Student t-distribution was developed by William Gosset who worked for the Guinness Brewery at the turn of the 20th century. He used statistics to monitor/improve the brewing process and was forbidden to publish anything he discovered. He published anyway, under the name "Student", from which the name of the distribution is derived. The t-value serves a role similar to the z-value when determining the margin of error for proportions. They are significantly different, though. At the 95% confidence level, there is only one z-value ($z = 1.96$), but the t-value depends on the sample size n.

When do we use t-values?

If we need to approximate the mean of a population, we can use the mean of a random sample. The techniques of this worksheet will help us find a margin of error for this approximation. If we know that the population is normally distributed, we can use the methods described here. If we don't know that the population is normally distributed, we can use these methods as long as our sample size is $n > 30$.

Most statistics textbooks come with printed tables of t-values. It can also be determined using technology. To determine the t-value, we need to know:

- the confidence level CL and

- the "degrees of freedom", which is $n - 1$

Important: Sources of t-values (whether tables or technology) use the confidence level CL differently. Be sure to understand how CL is used before using a particular source.

Computing t-values in Excel : the T.INV.2T Function

To compute the appropriate t-value, we will use the T.INV.2T command in Excel. The general form of the T.INV.2T command is T.INV.2T(1-confidence level, degrees of freedom). For a confidence level of CL with a sample size of n, we find

$$t = \text{T.INV.2T}(1 - CL, n - 1).$$

4. In a blank Excel worksheet, compute the t-value for the 95% confidence level with a sample size of $n = 20$. (The 95% confidence level corresponds to $CL = 0.95$.)

5. Compute the t-values that correspond to the following situations.

   (a) Sample size of $n = 40$ at the 90% confidence level.

   (If your answer is $t = 1.683851$, you likely entered 40, not 39 for the degrees of freedom. If your answer is $t = 0.126482$, you likely entered $CL = 0.90$ for the probability, not $1 - CL = 0.10$. You should get $t = 1.684875$.)

   (b) Sample size of $n = 40$ at the 95% confidence level.

   (c) Sample size of $n = 40$ at the 99% confidence level.

   (d) Sample size of $n = 100$ at the 95% confidence level.

   (e) Sample size of $n = 1,000$ at the 95% confidence level.

6. (a) In parts (a) through (c) above, did t get larger or smaller as the confidence level increased? What does this mean about the corresponding size of the confidence interval: does it get larger or smaller?

   (b) In parts (d) and (e) above, did t get larger or smaller as n increased from 100 to 1,000? What does this mean about the corresponding size of the confidence interval: does it get larger or smaller?

To gain an appreciation of the power and purpose of the confidence interval, open the Excel worksheet CI_Means of MtM_Unit3b_CourseContent.xlsx.

- In Column B, 1,000 items are measured and their values are given, randomly generated to follow a particular distribution.

- The mean of this population is given in Row 3.

- The first 50 items are sampled, and the sample mean is given in Row 4. Both numbers are likely near 50 when you open the workbook; refreshing the spreadsheet (by using the F9 refresh command) or entering any value in any cell will recompute the random numbers and change the means.

- The standard deviation of the sample is given in Row 5.

- In Row 6, the *t*-value corresponding to an 80% confidence level and a sample size of 50 is computed.

- In Row 7, the error for the 80% confidence interval is computed.

- You will soon be asked to fill in a formula for Row 9.

- The absolute value of the difference between the sample mean and the population mean is given in Row 8.

We will generate the confidence interval at the 80% confidence level. To do so, we need to determine the *t*-value and the margin of error, *E*.

7. Look at the formula in cell B6. Why does it use the value of 0.2? Why does it use the value of 49?

8. Look at the formula in cell B7. What does it multiply and divide?

9. We want Excel to determine when the population mean falls within the confidence interval. That is, we want determine if the difference between the sample and population means is less than *E*. (The difference is already computed for you in cell B8.)

   In cell B9, enter the function =if(B8<B7, ''Yes'', ''No''). What does this function do?

10. Refresh the worksheet a number of times to see if Yes and No are returned correctly. Is it working as you expect it to?

Click & drag all of the formulas in Column B (Row 3 down to Row 1010) to the right so your worksheet has 20 columns of trials. In each column, you should have 1,000 sample values of a population created, the population and sample means computed, the margin of error *E* calculated, etc.

11. Look across Row 9 at the Yes's and No's. (Recall: 'Yes' means the population mean *does* fall within the confidence interval.) Refresh the worksheet several times and observe the results. Does the population mean fall within the confidence interval about 80% of the time? About how many No's did you see each time you refreshed the worksheet?

Creating & Using Confidence Intervals

There are many software tools available (from handheld calculators to websites online) that can create a confidence interval given the necessary data. One needs only to supply the sample size n, the sample mean $\bar{x}$, and the sample standard deviation s. We will use the Conf. Interval Mean tab in the Statistics Calculator.xlsx spreadsheet as our confidence interval computational tool.

12. About 400 people participated in a study that tested the cognitive outcomes of preschool children whose mothers used cocaine while pregnant. The weight and head circumference of each child were taken at birth; such measurements of size are often used as proxies of a baby's general health.[2]

    (a) In the study, 186 babies were born to mothers who had not used cocaine (the control group). The mean birth weight of these babies was $\bar{x} = 6.84$ lb, with a standard deviation of $s = 1.53$ lb.

    Using this data, construct the 95% confidence interval for the mean birth weight of babies without prenatal exposure to cocaine.

    (b) In the study, 190 babies had prenatal exposure to cocaine. The mean birth weight of these babies was $\bar{x} = 5.95$ lb, with a standard deviation of $s = 1.42$ lb.

    Using this data, construct the 95% confidence interval for the mean birth weight of babies with prenatal exposure to cocaine.

    (c) **Application:** Based on your confidence intervals, does it seem likely that babies with prenatal exposure to cocaine have a lower birth weight than babies without prenatal cocaine exposure?

13. In the same study cited in Problem 12, the circumference of the baby's head at birth was measured.

    (a) The mean head circumference of babies without prenatal cocaine exposure was $\bar{x} = 33.5$ cm, with $s = 2.4$ cm. Construct the 99% confidence interval for the mean population head circumference at birth.

    (b) The mean head circumference of babies with prenatal cocaine exposure was $\bar{x} = 32.2$ cm, with $s = 2.1$ cm. Construct the 99% confidence interval for the mean population head circumference at birth.

    (c) **Application:** Does it seem likely that babies with prenatal cocaine exposure have smaller heads at birth than babies without prenatal exposure to cocaine?

In the previous two examples, notice that the only conclusion we could make is that it *seems likely* that babies with prenatal cocaine exposure had lower birth weights and smaller heads than babies without prenatal cocaine exposure. In order to make a stronger, more definitive conclusion, we need some more sophisticated statistical tools (which we will look at in the next module).

---

[2] See "Cognitive Outcomes of Preschool Children With Prenatal Cocaine Exposure," by Singer et al., *Journal of the American Medical Association*, Vol. 291, No. 20.

14. Two (fictitious) diet plans are compared in a study conducted by university researchers funded by the National Institute of Health. The 32 randomly selected participants who adhered to Diet A lost an average of 10 lbs after 2 months with a standard deviation of 2.3 lbs, while the randomly selected 36 participants who adhered to Diet B lost an average of 12 lbs after 2 months with a standard deviation of 3.1 lbs.

   (a) Compute the 95% confidence intervals for the mean population weight loss for each diet.

   (b) Is it accurate to say that "In this study, adherents of Diet B lost more weight, on average, than followers of Diet A."? Why/why not?

   Using confidence intervals, we have some evidence to support the conclusion that followers of Diet B lost more weight (on average) than followers of Diet A; however, it is unclear whether or not this difference is significant.

   (c) Compute the 99% confidence intervals for the mean population weight loss for each diet.

   (d) Is it fair to say that "In general, followers of Diet B will lose more weight, on average, than followers of Diet A."? Why/why not?

   We have evidence that it is likely that followers of Diet B will lose more weight than followers of Diet A because the true mean weight loss for each diet plan likely falls in confidence intervals that do not overlap. On the other hand, the 99% confidence intervals *do* overlap. Thus, we could conclude something along the lines of "We are 95% sure that the mean loss for Diet A adherents is less than the mean loss for Diet B adherents." We couldn't state "We are 99% sure …"

   *** **Check in with your instructor.**

Review and Reflect

Take a moment to think back on this section. What were the main ideas? What did you find most interesting?

-

-

-

-

-

Mean Confidence Interval Summary

- If a population's mean μ needs to be approximated, one can take a random sample and measure the sample's mean $\bar{x}$.

- The sample mean $\bar{x}$ is our best estimate of the value of μ. To get a better idea of how good this estimate is, we can construct a confidence interval.

- The three main factors influencing the size of the confidence interval (determined by its error E) are:

    - The sample size n: increasing n decreases E,

    - The sample standard deviation s: if s is large, then E will be, too; and

    - The confidence level: increasing the confidence level increases E.

- Perhaps surprisingly, the size of the population N does not effect the error E. In other words, we need not try to sample a certain *percentage* of the population to get a good sample. We just need to sample a good *number* n.

- If the confidence intervals for two different groups do not overlap, one has evidence that the means of those two groups are statistically different.

Assignment: Airline Overselling

Virginia Airlines, which only flies 175-seater single-class Boeing 737-800s, has a policy of selling 200 tickets for each flight. This is because there is a chance that someone who booked the flight doesn't make the plane. The Chief Operations Officer (COO) is interested in knowing if their current policies and associated costs are best. You may assume the following to be fixed in this analysis:

- Virginia Airlines sells 200 seats for each flight, and each ticket is $250.

- There is a 7% chance that any individual fails to show up for their flight.

- If more than 175 people show up, then anyone who doesn't fit on that flight is bumped. The airline incurs an average cost of $400 per bumped passenger. This $400 includes the cost of re-booking them on another flight and any inconvenience payments to the passenger.

- The cost of operating for each flight is $40,000.

You have been hired as a consultant to assess the current policy and make recommendations. Your consulting team has built an Excel spreadsheet to help analyze the problem (see CI_Airlines of MtM_Unit3b_CourseContent.xlsx). This spreadsheet simulates 1000 flights, looking to see how much profit is made based on how many of the ticketed passengers show up. Take some time to familiarize yourself with the spreadsheet.

Issues to address and a letter to Virginia Airlines for you to complete follow.

Issues

1. **Assessment of the existing policy**

   Based on a set of simulations, come up with a 95% confidence interval on the expected profit using the existing policy. Remember that to determine a confidence interval, you will need both the mean and the standard deviation. One of these has been calculated for you, and you need fill in the appropriate equation in Cell B3 to calculate the other. (Hint: you might want to look at what is in Cell B4 to see how the standard deviation is being calculated.) You will need to use your statistics calculator Excel file to generate the confidence interval.

   For reference later, insert your confidence interval here:

2. **Explore different results based on number of tickets sold**

   Keeping all of the other factors the same (ticket price, the number of seats on the plane, the cost per bumped passenger, or the likelihood of a passenger missing the flight), suppose you changed the number of tickets sold (up or down).

   What happens to your answer from question 1?

   Fill in the cells in the table below for ticket sales of 180 and 210, and (at least) three of your own choices for number of tickets sold.

# of tickets sold	Mean Profit	Std. Dev. of Profit	95% Confidence Interval
180			
210			

   (To see the effect of adding or removing passengers, remember that you can drag to fill/copy in Excel. You should not need to change any of the equations at the top of the spreadsheet – they are designed to update automatically based on the number of rows in your spreadsheet.)

3. **Best Policy**

   - What do you believe is the optimal number of tickets to sell for the flight in order to make the most profit? *Record number here for later reference.*

   - Explain your reasoning, making sure to give the 95% confidence interval on the expected profit using this optimal number of tickets.

4. **Letter to the Chief Operations Officer (COO)**

   Use your answers to complete the letter (next page) to the COO of Virginia Airlines.

Math that Matters Consulting Agency
insert date

Dr. Suzanne Marabam, Chief Operations Officer
Virginia Airlines Headquarters
One Skyway Road
Dulles, VA 20166

Dear Dr. Marabam,

We recently completed our analysis of Virginia Airlines' overbooking policy. It is our understanding that the current policy is to sell 200 tickets at a price of _____ for each of your 175-seat flights. It is also our understanding that when more than 175 passengers arrive for a flight, any bumped passenger causes the airline to incur a cost of _____. While passengers may be frustrated by being bumped from a flight for which they have bought a ticket, we realize that your policy allows a higher profit than simply selling 175 tickets because *insert rationale here*.

Based on these assumptions, our agency built a passenger-arrival simulator that assumes a 7% chance that each passenger might fail to arrive for the flight. We used this simulator to model _____ flights, and based on our simulation, we determined that, with 95% confidence, this policy should result in profits between _____ and _____.

We then modified our simulator to understand how the airline's profits would change if the number of tickets sold were updated in your overbooking policy. Based on our analysis, we found that the optimal number of tickets to sell on each flight is _____. By selling _____ tickets, we are 95% confident that this policy will result in profits between _____ and _____.

Therefore, our official recommendation is that you change your overbooking policy to:

We hope that this analysis is helpful, and we hope that you will keep Math that Matters Consulting in mind for any future analyses that you may need.

Respectfully Submitted,

_____

Exercises 4.4

1. If we want to determine the size of the confidence interval for a population mean, which of the following statistics would impact the interval size? Select all that apply

   (a) sample standard deviation

   (b) sample mean

   (c) population mean

   (d) sample size

   (e) population size

   (f) appropriate z-value

   (g) appropriate t-value

2. In a 2017 study about the sleep habits of wild, free–roaming African elephants, author Paul Manger records that over a period of 35 days, one elephant matriarch, matriarch A, slept an average of 2.3 hours a day (with s = 1.3 hr) and another matriarch, matriarch B, slept an average of 1.8 hours each day (with s= 1 hr). (This study suggests that elephants sleep the least of all recorded mammals.)

   (a) Viewing the recorded sleep times of each matriarch as coming from a random sample, construct a 95% confidence interval for the true mean hours of sleep matriarch A gets each day.

   (b) Viewing the recorded sleep times of each matriarch as coming from a random sample, construct a 95% confidence interval for the true mean hours of sleep matriarch B gets each day.

   (c) Can we say at a 95% confidence level that the matriarch B receives less sleep per day than matriarch A?

      i. Yes, the mean for matriarch B is less than the mean for matriarch A.

      ii. No, the two standard deviations are almost equal.

      iii. Yes, the confidence interval for matriarch B is different than the confidence interval for matriarch A.

      iv. No, the confidence level is the same for both matriarchs.

      v. No, the confidence intervals for the matriarchs overlap.

   (d) Some media outlets reported on this result with statements similar to "A new study shows that African elephants sleep an average of 2 hours a day." Is such a statement a reasonable synopsis of the study?

      i. Yes, the confidence intervals support this claim.

      ii. No, the confidence intervals do not support this claim.

      iii. No, the confidence intervals are inconclusive.

3. A paper published in 1984 studied the effect of zinc lozenges on the duration of the common cold. The results of this study spurred further research and led to the rise of over-the-counter zinc-based cold remedies. Based on the data presented in the paper, one can approximate the mean length of cold symptoms experienced by the 37 patients receiving zinc lozenges was 4.37 days (with a standard deviation of 3.74 days), whereas the 28 patients receiving a placebo had a mean length of cold symptoms of 9.08 days (with a standard deviation of 7.14 days). Assume that the number of days of experiencing cold symptoms is normally distributed.

   (a) Construct the 95% confidence interval for the mean number of days a patient experienced cold symptoms for the group who used zinc lozenges.

   (b) Construct the 95% confidence interval for the mean number of days a patient experienced cold symptoms for the group who were given a placebo.

   (c) Do the results of this study seem to support the idea that the patients taking zinc lozenges truly experienced cold symptoms for fewer days, on average, than those taking placebo lozenges?

      i. Yes, the entire confidence interval for the lozenge group is below the confidence interval for the placebo group.

      ii. No, the confidence level is the same for both groups.

      iii. Yes, the mean for the lozenge group is less than the mean for the placebo group.

      iv. Yes, the two standard deviation for the lozenge group is much smaller than the placebo group.

4. In "How Fair Shares Compare: Experimental Evidence from Two Cultures", economist Pamela Jakiela of the University of Maryland describes a study in which university undergraduate students in California and citizens of a remote Kenyan village are given an opportunity to win a reward, based on chance, then share a portion of their reward. The paper conveys that the 533 Kenyans shared 26.5% of their reward, on average, whereas the 185 university students shared, on average, 19.9% of their reward. The paper states that these differences were statistically significant using complex statistical tools (the standard deviations are not given).

   (a) How big would the standard deviations, in percent form, need to be in order for the confidence intervals of these two mean to overlap at a 95% confidence level? (Assume that the percentage shared for each population is normally distributed and that the standard deviations of the samples are the same.)

   (b) Is it likely that the standard deviation is that large? What does that tell us?

   (c) Dr. Jekeila also allowed participants to earn a reward, through effort, then share. (Recall that earlier, the reward was a result of chance). On average, the Kenyans shared 22.2% of their earned reward, while the university students shared 13.5% of their earnings. Assume that the standard deviations for both samples is 2% and that the same number of Kenyans and students were observed.

   How small would the sample sizes need to be for the confidence intervals of each mean to overlap?

   (d) Since the actual sample sizes were not as small as your previous answer, can one safely conclude that "The Kenyan participants shared a higher percentage of their earnings than the university students?" Select all that apply.

      i. Yes, the confidence intervals at the 95% confidence do not overlap.

      ii. No, the confidence intervals at the 95% confidence overlap.

      iii. Yes, the confidence intervals at the 99% confidence levels do not overlap.

      iv. No, the confidence intervals at the 99% confidence levels overlap.

5. A company is interested in understanding the effectiveness of a weight loss drug that it recently developed. To this end, the company conducted a clinical trial in which it observed the number of people in the trial who lost more than 30 lbs within 6 months of using the drug (combined with a specified diet and exercise regimen).

   Based on this information, which of the following types of confidence intervals would best help the company gauge the effectiveness of the medication?

   (a) A 90% confidence interval for the mean weight lost by the clinical trial participants in 6 months.

   (b) A 90% confidence interval for the proportion of clinical trial participants who lost less than 30 lbs in 6 months.

   (c) A 90% confidence interval for the proportion of clinical trial participants who lost more than 30 lbs in 6 months.

   (d) A 90% confidence interval for the average number of clinical trial participants who lost more than 30 lbs in 6 months.

6. Your friend claims that the average height of a male is 72 inches. You want to test their claim and take a simple random sample of 10 males and find that the mean height is 69.8 inches with a standard deviation of 2.3 inches.

   (a) Construct the 90% confidence interval for the mean height of males.

   (b) Is your friend's claim supported through your confidence interval result? Defend your answer.

4.5   An Introduction to Hypothesis Testing

A lady claimed she could tell the difference between milk poured into tea and tea poured into milk. To test her claim, she was put to the test: four cups of "tea poured into milk" and four cups of "milk poured into tea" were prepared and placed in a random order. She then had to determine if the tea, or milk, was poured in first for each cup. It turns out that there are 70 possible arrangements of the cups, and so if she was just guessing, she only had a 1/70 chance, or 1.4% chance, of getting it right.

This probability of something happening just by chance is called the *P*-value. When there is a claim we want to test, we collect some data about the situation, and we use that data to calculate the *P*-value (that is, the likelihood that what we observed happened by chance). If that *P*-value is small, it implies that what we observed was not just random chance – maybe something special happened and the claim just might be true!

In the case of the lady and her tea, suppose she did correctly identify all 8 cups. The chance of her accomplishing this by just guessing is 1.4%. Since most people would agree that that is a low percentage, it serves as evidence that she truly can tell the difference between the cups of tea.

Let's walk through another example. Suppose we want to determine if a coin is fair (meaning we are going to flip it, and it should land on heads and tails roughly the same number of times).

1. If we flipped the coin just twice, and it landed on heads both times, do you think we have enough data to say whether or not the coin is fair? Why or why not?

2. Hopefully, you decided that we can't yet make a confident decision. What would you propose we do so that we can be more confident in a claim that a coin is/isn't fair?

OK, we need more flips! Let's look at two cases.

Case 1. Suppose we flipped the coin 100 times, and it came up heads 85 times. This seems pretty extreme, right?

3. What is the proportion of flips that landed on heads?

4. Is it *possible* that this could happen with a fair coin?

5. Is it *likely* that this happened with a fair coin?

6. It turns out that there is less than a 0.0000000003% chance that this could happen randomly! Would you want to flip this coin on any bet if you could call heads?

Case 2. That coin didn't seem very fair. We don't *know* that it is unfair, but it seems unlikely. So, let's get a new coin. Suppose we flipped this new coin 100 times, and it landed on heads 62 times. Remember that for a fair coin, we would expect the proportion of heads to be 0.5, or for 100 tosses, we would expect 50 heads. It turns out that the likelihood of getting 62 or more heads if the coin is fair is $P = 0.016$. That means that there is only a 1.6% chance of the coin landing on at least 62 heads in 100 flips by chance. We need to make a decision: is a 1.6% chance unusual enough for us to conclude the coin is unfair? Such a decision often depends on the stakes involved.

7. If you could bet someone $0.25 that the coin is unfair, would you do it?

8. Does your answer change if it was a $1000 bet?

9. Suppose now a coin is flipped 100 times which landed on heads 58 times. You are told the probability of something as extreme as this happening with a fair coin is about 11%. Would you be willing to bet $1000 that the coin is unfair?

When we are prepared to make a decision about whether we think an event has happened by chance, we need to be able to compare a *P*-value to a threshold, called a *significance level*, which depends on how sure we want to be. In the case of the 25-cent bet, we don't need to be completely convinced that the coin is unfair. One might even say "I'd be willing to bet $5 if there was less than a 10% chance the coin was fair." And since we just saw a particular coin turn up heads 62 times out of 100, and the chances of that happening at random is about 1.6%, we'd be willing to make a $5 bet that the coin is unfair, since 1.6% is less than our 10% threshold.

However, we may not be willing to put up with as much uncertainty in the case where a thousand dollars is on the line. We might want to be 99% confident that the coin is unfair, meaning we are willing to accept that the coin favors heads only if there's less than a 1% chance that the coin landed heads on 62 out of 100 flips completely by chance. Since 1.6% lies above our new threshold of 1%, we do not have sufficient evidence to conclude that the coin is unfair. Thus, based on this logic, we should probably not choose to take the bet.

Important terms and a mini-summary:

- An event is observed (such as, 62 heads from 100 coin flips). A *P-value* is the probability that an event *at least as extreme* as the one observed happens purely by random chance.

- A *significance level* is a measure of the tolerance one has for thinking something significant has happened when, in reality, it was the result of random chance.

- If the *P*-value is LOWER than the significance level, then the probability that the event happened by random chance is lower than the tolerance; we will conclude that something special happened. (For future reference, we will later use the phrase "reject the null hypothesis.")

- If the *P*-value is HIGHER than the significance level, then the probability that the event happened by random chance is higher than the tolerance; we won't conclude something special happened. (For future reference, we will later use the phrase "fail to reject the null hypothesis.")

The process of observing an event, calculating the probability of that event (or something more extreme) happening, and comparing that probability to a significance level is called "performing a *hypothesis test*." Hypothesis testing is similar to a court trial. Consider the scenario where a defendant is accused of stealing a $20 bill from a lady's purse. We begin (in the U.S.) by assuming the defendant is innocent. We consider evidence that the defendant is guilty. Let's say that the evidence amounts to:

- the defendant was seen standing next to the lady's purse, and

- the defendant later used a $20 bill to buy ice cream.

Is that enough evidence to declare the defendant guilty? Probably not. One can stand near someone's purse and later use a $20 bill without being guilty of theft. The likelihood of this being "random chance" is probably *higher* than our "significance level," our tolerance level for thinking something special has happened. Since the probability of randomness explaining the defendant's behavior is higher than our tolerance, we *fail to reject* the notion that he is innocent. We haven't *proven* he is innocent; we failed to find sufficient evidence to conclude otherwise.

Now consider a similar situation: a man is accused of stealing a lady's wallet, monogrammed with her initials, from her purse. The evidence amounts to:

- the defendant was seen standing next to the lady's purse, and

- the defendant is soon after seen holding a wallet with her initials on it.

Now the chance of this being "random chance" seems considerably lower. Of course, it could be "random"; perhaps he is holding his wife's wallet, who happens to have the same initials, etc. But that seems unlikely. We would probably find the defendant guilty: the probability that the observed event happened due to chance is *lower* than our "significance level," our tolerance level for thinking something special has happened. We would *reject* the claim to his innocence, and conclude he is guilty.

In court, our presumption of innocence is a presumption that "nothing special occurred with the defendant." In hypothesis testing, we call this the *null hypothesis*. The *alternate hypothesis* is that something significant happened. In the case of court, the alternate conclusion to innocence is guilt.

Consider flipping a coin 100 times and getting 62 heads. Our experience is that coins are fair, so our null hypothesis will be "the coin is fair, showing heads half the time." The alternate hypothesis is "the coin shows heads more than half the time." Since the probability that a fair coin will show at least 62 heads by random chance is $P = 1.6\%$, many would conclude to "reject the null hypothesis", as 1.6% is lower than many people's tolerance, or significance, level.

Answer the following questions.

10. So, with a *P*-value of 1.6% and a significance level of 5%, we:

    (a) Reject the null; the coin is probably unfair

    (b) Fail to reject the null; we cannot conclude the coin is unfair.

11. So, with a *P*-value of 1.6% and a significance level of 1%, we:

    (a) Reject the null; the coin is probably unfair

    (b) Fail to reject the null; we cannot conclude the coin is unfair.

*** **Check in with your instructor.**

You should have answered (a) and (b) for problems 10 and 11, respectively. For problem 10, we see that the *P*-value of of 1.6% is below the significance level of 5%. Thus there is enough evidence to suggest that something other than the null hypothesis has occurred, and we reject the null hypothesis. In problem 11, we require more reasonable doubt than before (hence the 1% significance level). Now our *P*-value is greater than the significance level, suggesting that we do not have sufficient evidence to reject the null hypothesis. Thus we fail to reject the null hypothesis and conclude that the coin could probably be fair.

Let's look at four examples. These examples will use the following terms we have not yet defined: *testable question*, *1-sample*, and *2-sample*. You may be able to discover their meaning by context; we use them now so these examples can be used later for review.

Example 1

Research Issue: Comparing divorce rates of 2020 and 1950
Claim: The percent of marriages that ended in divorce in 2020 is different than it was in 1950, which was 30.8%.
Testable Question: Is the proportion of marriages that end in divorce in 2020 different than 30.8%?
Null Hypothesis: The proportion p of marriages ending in divorce in 2020 is 30.8%.
$p = 0.308$
Alternative Hypothesis: The proportion p of marriages ending in divorce in 2020 is different than 30.8%.
$p \neq 0.308$
Type of Test: Proportion, 1-sample
P-value: 0.016
Significance Level: 5%

12. **Statistical Conclusion:** Using this P-value and significance level, our statistical conclusion is (choose one):

   (a) Since the P-value is lower than the significance level, there is enough evidence to reject the null. (Reject the null)

   (b) Since the P-value is lower than the significance level, there is not enough evidence to reject the null. (Fail to reject the null)

13. **Contextualized Conclusion:** Now, we need to put the statistical conclusion into context, and we can say (choose one):

   (a) There is sufficient evidence to support the claim that the proportion of divorces was not the same in 2020 as it was in 1950.

   (b) There is not sufficient evidence to support the claim that the rate of divorce in 2020 is different than it was in 1950.

Example 2

Research Issue: Meditation lowering heart rates
Claim: A person who meditates has a resting heart rate that is lower than the average adult resting heart rate of 78 bpm.
Testable Question: Is the mean heart rate of someone meditating lower than 78 bpm?
Null Hypothesis: $\mu \geq 78$
Alternative Hypothesis: $\mu < 78$
Type of Test: Mean, 1-sample
P-value: 0.09
Significance Level: 5%

14. **Statistical Conclusion:** Using this P-value and significance level, our statistical conclusion is (choose one):

   (a) Since the P-value is lower than the significance level, there is enough evidence to reject the null. (Reject the null)

   (b) Since the P-value is lower than the significance level, there is not enough evidence to reject the null. (Fail to reject the null)

15. **Contextualized Conclusion:** Now, we need to put the statistical conclusion into context, and we can say (choose one):

   (a) There is sufficient evidence to support the claim that meditating lowers one's heart rate.

   (b) There is not sufficient evidence to support the claim that meditating lowers one's heart rate.

Example 3

Research Issue: Vitamin C preventing colds
Claim: Taking Vitamin C in the winter makes you less likely to catch a cold than the average person, where on average 3.8% of the population gets a winter cold.
Testable Question: Is the proportion of Vitamin C takers who catch a cold lower than 0.038?
Null Hypothesis: $p \geq 0.038$
Alternative Hypothesis: $p < 0.038$
Type of Test: Proportion, 1-sample
P-value: 0.09
Significance Level: 10%

16. **Statistical Conclusion:** Using this *P*-value and significance level, our statistical conclusion is (choose one):

    (a) Since the *P*-value is lower than the significance level, there is enough evidence to reject the null. (Reject the null)

    (b) Since the *P*-value is lower than the significance level, there is not enough evidence to reject the null. (Fail to reject the null)

17. **Contextualized Conclusion:** Now, we need to put the statistical conclusion into context, and we can say (choose one):

    (a) There is sufficient evidence to support the claim that Vitamin C prevents colds.

    (b) There is not sufficient evidence to support the claim that Vitamin C prevents colds.

Example 4:

Research Issue: Math majors getting honors
Claim: Math majors are more likely to graduate with honors.
Testable Question: Is the proportion of graduating math majors earning honors greater than the proportion of all college graduates earning honors?
Null Hypothesis: $p_1 \leq p_2$
Alternative Hypothesis: $p_1 > p_2$
Type of Test: Proportion, 2-sample
P-value: 0.047
Significance Level: 5%

18. Using this *P*-value and significance level, our statistical conclusion is (choose one):

    (a) Since the *P*-value is lower than the significance level, there is enough evidence to reject the null. (Reject the null)

    (b) Since the *P*-value is lower than the significance level, there is not enough evidence to reject the null. (Fail to reject the null)

19. Now, we need to put the statistical conclusion into context, and we can say (choose one):

    (a) There is sufficient evidence to support the claim that math majors are more likely to earn honors.

    (b) There is not sufficient evidence to support the claim that math major are more likely to graduate with honors.

*** **Check in with your instructor.**

Review and Reflect

Take a moment to think back on this section. What were the main ideas? What did you find most interesting?

-

-

-

-

-

Hypothesis Testing – Introduction Summary

- The *P-value* is the measure of how likely it is that something happened by chance.

- The *significance level* is a measure of the tolerance one has for accepting a random event as being non-random.

- At the moment, we have the following understanding of the following terms:

  - The *null hypothesis* is a statement that essentially says "nothing significant or different has occurred."
  - The *alternate hypothesis* is a statement that essentially says "something significant or different has occurred."

- If the *P*-value of an event is higher than the significance level, then the probability that the event occurred at random is higher than our tolerance. We cannot conclude something special has happened; we *fail to reject the null hypothesis*.

- If the *P*-value of an event is lower than the significance level, then the probability that the event occurred at random is lower than our tolerance. We conclude something significant has happened; we *reject the null hypothesis*.

- A useful rhyming aid to help remember the above scenario: "If *P* is low, the null must go!"

Exercises 4.5

1. The *P*-value is (select all correct answers):

   (a) A probability

   (b) Must be one of these values: 0.01, 0.05, 0.1

   (c) Is compared to the significance level to decide if you will reject or fail to reject the null hypothesis

2. True or False: If a result is statistically significant at the 5% level, then it is always statistically significant at the 1% level.

3. True or False: If a result is statistically significant at the 1% level, then it is always statistically significant at the 5% level.

4. The pharmaceutical company Moderna developed a vaccine for COVID-19 and ran clinical trials on its effectiveness. The trial showed a much lower percentage of people who were vaccinated contracted Covid than those who were given a placebo, but this could have been the result of random chance.

   (a) Since millions of people around the world could end up taking this vaccine, how low should the significance level be?

   (b) Moderna published its data, and stated that the probability its good results were due to chance was $P < 0.01\%$. Does this seem low enough to recommend this vaccine to the general public?

5. You are studying to see if philosophy majors have higher IQs than the general population. You conduct an experiment, collecting IQs of philosophy majors and members of the general public. In your data, you find the average IQ of the philosophy majors is higher than the average IQ of the general public, and the probability that this result is due to chance is 0.04. What is your statistical conclusion at the 5% significance level?

   (a) Reject the null hypothesis.

   (b) Fail to reject the null hypothesis.

6. You are studying to see if people that use Crest toothpaste have less cavities than people who use Colgate toothpaste. Suppose you conduct an experiment, and in your study the Crest users have fewer cavities than the Colgate users. You find that the probability of this happening by chance is $P = 0.07$. What is your contextual conclusion at the 5% significance level?

   (a) The evidence suggests that Crest users have fewer cavities than Colgate users.

   (b) There is not enough evidence to suggest that Crest users have fewer cavities than Colgate users.

   (c) You cannot reach a conclusion without knowing the mean number of cavities of each sample.

   (d) Crest is a better toothpaste.

4.6 Designing Hypothesis Tests

Last class, we learned how to interpret hypothesis tests by comparing the P-value and the significance level. We also saw that there was some vocabulary that we used but never really defined. Today, we will formalize some terms that we saw last class: null hypothesis, alternative hypothesis, and testable question.

Let's start by looking at the null hypothesis and alternative hypothesis. The null is the hypothesis that nothing special is happening; that things are just as we would expect. Here are a few examples:

- If we are flipping a coin, the null hypothesis is that no one did anything special to the coin, and it is fair.

- If we are looking at the rate of divorces between two years, the null hypothesis is that they would be the same – that nothing special happened to cause a change.

- If we are testing whether or not Crest whitens teeth better than Colgate, the null hypothesis is that the Crest doesn't do anything better/worse than Colgate.

In contrast, the alternative hypothesis represents the claim that we want to test. This is the claim that something special happened.

- The coin is unfair and gives a noticeably different number of heads and tails (there is something special about that coin).

- The divorce rates are not the same.

- Crest whitens better than Colgate.

1. Consider the claim, "Eating eggs after a workout significantly increases muscle mass." Which of the following is the null hypothesis and which is the alternative hypothesis?

    (a) The average increase in muscle mass is the same (or lower) for people who eat eggs after a workout when compared with people who don't.

    (b) The average increase in muscle mass is greater for people who eat eggs after a workout when compared with people who don't.

Consider the null and alternate hypotheses given in the examples in the previous section. They are listed in the table below, using mathematical notation instead of using words. Here we also use "H_0" to represent the null hypothesis, and "H_1" to represent the alternate hypothesis.

Example Claim	Null H_0	Alt H_1
Divorce proportion	$p = 0.308$	$p \neq 0.308$
Meditation heart rate	$\mu \geq 78$	$\mu < 78$
Vitamin C and colds	$p \geq 0.308$	$p < 0.0308$
Math majors with honors	$p_1 \leq p_2$	$p_1 > p_2$

2. What do all the null hypotheses have in common that cause them to standout from the alternative hypotheses?

*** Check in with your instructor.

Hypothesis & Testable Question Matching Activity

The worksheet HT_Matching in the Excel workbook MtM_Unit3b_CourseContent.xlsx contains an activity designed to help one understand the components of a hypothesis test.

Only move on after you have completed a version of the activity.

In the activity, you were given a number of questions that were labelled *testable questions*, but we hadn't yet defined that term. We do so now; a testable question is:

- a question,

- answerable with Yes or No,

- that clearly indicates the statistic that needs to be computed from data.

You should notice that all the testable questions in the activity follow the same basic format:

Is {name of statistic} {greater than, less than, equal to/not equal to} {comparison value or name of second statistic}?

For instance, one testable question from the activity is "Is the average lifespan of a male smoker less than 82.3 years?" Notice how it fits the above pattern with the addition of brackets: "Is {the average lifespan of a male smoker} {less than} {82.3 years}? Note too that this question fulfills the bulleted requirements above: it is a question, it has a Yes or No answer, and it clearly states we are to find an average and compare it to 82.3.

Note that there are other ways to word testable questions, and you may see these in future classes, research projects, or your work one day. However, this format is a fail-safe way of wording testable questions, so this is what we will use in this class.

3. Circle each of the testable questions on this list. Choose at least one question that is NOT a testable question and rewrite it as a testable question.

    (a) Is the mean credit score for people living in Virginia higher than the national average of 700?

    (b) Are dolphins smarter than whales?

    (c) Is Vitamin C effective at reducing colds?

    (d) Is the proportion of students in the U.S. who enter law school with a non-STEM degree greater than the proportion of students who enter with a STEM degree?

    (e) Is the average American drinking at least 4 cups of water per day?

    (f) Is the proportion of students who participated in an internship during college that resulted in post-graduate employment greater than 50%?

    (g) Is the mean SAT score for homeschooled students lower than the mean SAT score for non-homeschooled students?

    (h) Is basketball more popular than baseball?

Now let's work through an example that combines today's work with the interpretation work we did in the previous section. Below is a hypothesis test with some parts completed and other parts that you need to answer or complete.

Research issue: Weight loss for diet vs. exercise
Claim: People who exercise lose more weight than those who diet.

4. **Testable question:** Select the testable question from the list below

    (a) Do people who exercise lose more weight than those who diet?

    (b) Is the proportion of people who exercise that lose more than 20 lbs in a year greater than the proportion of people who diet that lose more than 20 lbs for a year?

(c) Is the mean weight loss for people who exercise in a year greater than the average weight loss for people who diet for a year?

(d) Is weight loss proportional to exercise or dieting?

5. Null hypothesis: Fill in the blank to write the null hypothesis in symbols

$H_0 : \mu_1$_____

6. Alternative hypothesis: Fill in the blank to write the alternative hypothesis in symbols

$H_1 : \mu_1$_____

7. Suppose that after collecting data and conducting a hypothesis test, you obtain a P-value of 0.013. If you use a significance level of 10% for your study, what is your statistical conclusion?

(a) Reject the null hypothesis.

(b) Fail to reject the null hypothesis.

8. In your own words, what is the conclusion of this test in the context of the original research issue?

*** **Check in with your instructor.**

Review and Reflect

Take a moment to think back on this section. What were the main ideas? What did you find most interesting?

-

-

-

-

-

Hypothesis Testing – Design Summary

- A testable question is the foundation of a hypothesis test. It is a question, with a Yes or No answer, that clearly indicates the statistic that needs to be computed from data.

- Recall that if the *P*-value is *less than* the significance level,

    - the probability of what we observed happening because of random chance is *lower* than our threshold,

    - we *reject* the null hypothesis ("if *P* is low, the null must go."), and

    - our contextualized conclusion will use wording such as "There *is* sufficient evidence to conclude..."

- Recall that if the *P*-value is *greater* than the significance level,

    - the probability of what we observed happening because of random chance is *higher* than our threshold,

    - we *fail to reject* the null hypothesis, and

    - our contextualized conclusion will use wording such as "There *is not* sufficient evidence to conclude ..."

Exercises 4.6

1. Which of the following are examples of null hypotheses?

   (a) $H_0 : p \leq 0.7$

   (b) $H_0 : p < 0.7$

   (c) $H_0 : p = 0.7$

   (d) $H_0 : p \neq 0.7$

   (e) $H_0 : p \geq 0.7$

   (f) $H_0 : p < 0.7$

2. Given the null hypothesis $H_0 : \mu \leq 13$, what is the correct alternative hypothesis?

   (a) $H_1 : \mu \leq 13$

   (b) $H_1 : \mu < 13$

   (c) $H_1 : \mu = 13$

   (d) $H_1 : \mu \neq 13$

   (e) $H_1 : \mu \geq 13$

   (f) $H_1 : \mu > 13$

3. Crest claims that their toothpaste is better at preventing cavities than Colgate. Which of the following is a testable question that could be used to investigate this claim? (Select all that apply.)

   (a) Is the mean number of cavities of Colgate users greater than the mean number of cavities of Crest users?

   (b) Is Crest better than Colgate?

   (c) Is the mean number of cavities of Crest users less than the mean number of cavities of Colgate users?

   (d) Does Crest reduce the number of cavities?

   (e) Is the proportion of Crest users greater than the proportion of Colgate users?

4. If the probability of the observed statistic (P-value) is very low (lower than the significance level), what do you conclude regarding the null hypothesis?

   (a) The experiment is flawed and you need to either repeat it with a different sample or alter the design.

   (b) The experiment provided evidence to reject the null hypothesis.

   (c) The experiment did not provide sufficient evidence to reject the null hypothesis.

5. Suppose you want to know "Do people who have a high school education earn less than those who complete a 4-year college degree?"

   (a) Rewrite this question as a testable question.

   (b) Let μ_1 be the mean income of people who have a high school education and μ_2 be the mean income of people who have completed a 4-year college degree.

   What is the correct statement of the null hypothesis?

      i. $H_0 : \mu_1 \leq \mu_2$

      ii. $H_0 : \mu_1 = \mu_2$

      iii. $H_0 : \mu_1 \geq \mu_2$

      iv. $H_0 : \mu = 0.5$

   (c) What is the correct statment of the alternate hypothesis?

      i. $H_1 : \mu_1 < \mu_2$

      ii. $H_1 : \mu_1 \neq \mu_2$

      iii. $H_1 : \mu_1 > \mu_2$

      iv. $H_1 : \mu \neq 0.5$

6. Suppose that we would like to answer the following question: "Do most VMI cadets commission?"

    (a) Write this question as a testable question.

    (b) What would be the correct null hypothesis?

        i. $H_0 : p \leq 0.5$

        ii. $H_0 : p < 0.5$

        iii. $H_0 : p = 0.5$

        iv. $H_0 : p \neq 0.5$

        v. $H_0 : p \geq 0.5$

        vi. $H_0 : p > 0.5$

    (c) What would be the correct alternate hypothesis?

        i. $H_1 : p \leq 0.5$

        ii. $H_1 : p < 0.5$

        iii. $H_1 : p = 0.5$

        iv. $H_1 : p \neq 0.5$

        v. $H_1 : p \geq 0.5$

        vi. $H_1 : p > 0.5$

    (d) You sample VMI graduates and find that 55% of them commissioned, with $P = 0.13$. At the 5% significance level, what can we say? Choose all that apply.

        i. We reject the null hypothesis.

        ii. We fail to reject the null hypothesis.

        iii. There is insufficient evidence to conclude that more than half of VMI cadets commission.

        iv. There is sufficient evidence to conclude that more than half of VMI cadets commission.

7. When games were sampled throughout a season, it was found that the home team won 118 of 185 basketball games and the home team won 48 of 75 lacrosse games. Set up the null and alternative hypothesis to test the claim that the basketball team won a different proportion of home games than did the lacrosse team.

    (a) Null hypothesis

    (b) Alternative hypothesis

    (c) You run the hypothesis test and determine the P-value is 0.974. If you use a significance level of 5%, should you reject the null hypothesis or fail to reject the null hypothesis?

    (d) In your own words, what is the conclusion of this hypothesis test in the context of the original claim.

8. A dairy processing company claims that the amount of fat in the whole milk product is at least 25%. You suspect that is wrong and find a random sample of 41 milk containers and find a mean of 23% with a standard deviation of 8%. Set up the null and alternative hypothesis to test the claim that the amount of fat in whole milk is less than the advertised 25%.

    (a) Null hypothesis

    (b) Alternative hypothesis

    (c) You run the hypothesis test and determine the P-value is 0.059. If you use a significance level of 5%, should you reject the null hypothesis or fail to reject the null hypothesis?

    (d) In your own words, what is the conclusion of this hypothesis test in the context of the original claim.

4.7 Hypothesis Tests Involving Proportions and Means

We have learned how to interpret the results of a hypothesis test and how to take a research issue or claim and develop a testable question, a null hypothesis, and an alternative hypothesis. Today, we will learn the key steps to actually run a hypothesis test and compute a P-value.

Types of Hypothesis Tests

There are a lot of types of hypothesis tests depending on the statistic to be tested and the underlying distribution of the population. Depending on the one's field of study and the types of problems one might need to solve, one may use one type of test often and never need another type of test. The good news is that all hypothesis tests work pretty much the same way, and once one knows how to conduct one, other tests are easier to learn. We will only focus on the most fundamental hypothesis tests:

- a test for proportions (studied in this section)

- a test for means (studied in the this section), and

- a test for dependence (studied in the next section).

Testing for Proportions or Means

Consider the table below that revisits some of the claims presented in earlier sections. We identify for each whether the claim is testing a mean or a proportion.

Claim to be Tested	Statistic (Proportion or Mean)
The percent of marriages that end in divorce today is different than it was in 1950, which was 30.8%.	Proportion
A person who meditates has a resting heart rate that is lower than the average adult resting heart rate of 78 bpm.	Mean
Taking Vitamin C in the winter makes you less likely to catch a cold than the average person, and on average 3.8% of the population gets a winter cold.	Proportion (be careful on this one!)
Math majors are more likely to graduate with honors than physics majors.	Proportion
Cars on I-81 drive faster than cars on I-95.	Mean
Most cars on I-81 go faster than the speed limit.	Proportion

1. Looking at the table, what are some clues or key words you can use to help you determine whether a test is for proportions or means?

2. Using the clues or key words that you have identified, select whether each of the claims below should be addressed by using a test for means or a test for proportions.

Claim to be Tested	Statistic (Proportion or Mean)
The percentage of students who participated in and internship during college is greater than 50%.	P
Homeschooled students have lower SAT scores than students in public schools.	M
Students who learn an instrument in school are more likely to score higher than the average score of 531 on the Math SAT.	P
People under the age of 30 spend more time hiking than playing video games.	M
United Airlines has a higher chance of having on-time departures than Delta Airlines	M
Europeans drink more water a day than Americans.	M

Testing 1-sample or 2-samples

When running a hypothesis test, we are always comparing one value to another. Sometimes we collect data from one population, compute one statistic, then compare that value to a given value. This is a *1-sample test* as we've taken one sample. For instance, if we are testing the claim that "Less than half of Americans vote in a Presidential election," we could find the proportion of Americans who vote from one random sample.

Sometimes we collect data from two populations, compute a statistic from each sample, then compare these numbers. This is a *2-sample test* as we've taken two samples. For instance, if we are testing the claim that "Virginians are more likely to vote in a Presidential election than Texans", we would randomly sample two groups, Virginians and Texans, and compute the proportion of voters from each sample.

Consider the table below that again revisits some of the claims presented in earlier sections. We identify for each whether the claim is requires a 1-sample test or a 2-sample test.

Claim to be Tested	Number of Samples (1-sample or 2-sample)
The percent of marriages that end in divorce today is different than it was in 1950, which was 30.8%.	1-sample
A person who meditates has a resting heart rate that is lower than the average adult resting heart rate of 78 bpm.	1-sample
Taking Vitamin C in the winter makes you less likely to catch a cold than the average person, and on average 3.8% of the population gets a winter cold.	1-sample
Math majors are more likely to graduate with honors than physics majors.	2-sample
Cars on I-81 drive faster than cars on I-95.	2-sample
Most cars on I-81 go faster than the speed limit.	1-sample

3. Looking at the table, what are some clues or key words you can use to help you determine whether a test is a 1-sample or 2-sample test?

4. Using the clues or key words you have identified, select whether each of the claims below should be addressed by using a 1-sample test or a 2-sample test.

Claim to be Tested	Number of Samples (1-sample or 2-sample)
The percentage of students who participated in and internship during college is greater than 50%.	
Homeschooled students have lower SAT scores than students in public schools.	
Students who learn an instrument in school are more likely to score higher than the average score of 531 on the Math SAT.	
People under the age of 30 spend more time hiking than playing video games.	
United Airlines has a higher chance of having on-time departures than Delta Airlines	
Europeans drink more water a day than Americans.	

Putting it all together

We are finally ready to calculate P-values. In the past, one often had to do many hand calculations and use tables of numbers to compute P-values. Today, numerous software packages and online tool exist to make the computation of P-values much simpler. We will use the Excel file Statistics Calculator.xlsx (used previously to compute confidence intervals) to compute P-values.

The six tabs of this workbook are listed below.

- Conf. Interval Proportion

- Conf. Interval Means

- Hyp. Test – 1 Mean

- Hyp. Test – 2 Means

- Hyp. Test – 1 Proportion

- Hyp. Test – 2 Proportions

We already learned how to use the first two tabs to find confidence intervals in the last module, so here we focus on the hypothesis test tabs by looking at three examples.

5. For each of these claims, identify which Hyp. Test tab you should use based on whether you are testing for means or proportions, and whether you are running a 1-sample or 2-sample test.

Claim to be Tested	Spreadsheet Tab
Americans have higher cholesterol than the desired maximum of 200 milligrams per deciliter.	
A majority of people who sleep less than the average American (i.e. less than 6.8 hours) have been diagnosed with depression.	
People who include organic foods in their diets are less likely to have 2 or more colds in a year than those who do not.	

We will look at each claim a bit more closely and run a full hypothesis test.

Claim 1: Americans have higher cholesterol levels than the desired maximum of 200 milligrams per deciliter (mg/dL).

In order to test this claim, 841 Americans had their cholesterol levels tested. The average cholesterol level was reported to be 201 mg/dL with a standard deviation of 2 mg/dL.

6. Which of the following testable questions best addresses research Claim 1?

   (a) Is the percentage of Americans with cholesterol levels higher than 200 mg/dL higher than 50%?

   (b) Is the average number of Americans with cholesterol higher than 200 mg/dL greater than 841?

   (c) Is the average cholesterol level of an American greater than 200 mg/dL?

   (d) Is high cholesterol a problem for Americans?

7. Write the null and alternative hypotheses.

   $H_0 \quad\quad P \geq 200\,mg\,dl$

   $H_1 \quad p < 200\,mg\,dl$

The claim makes a statement about an *average* of *one group* of people. Thus we need a 1-sample means test. (Look back to Problem 5 to ensure the Hyp. Test - 1 Mean tab is indicated for this claim.)

When you open the Hyp. Test - 1 Mean tab, you should see four cells at the top that you need to fill in. We will look at each in turn.

8. The first cell is labeled "Sample Mean: $\bar{x}$", where $\bar{x}$ is the mean American cholesterol level in your sample. What value should you type into Cell B1 to test Claim 1?

9. The second cell is labeled "Sample Std. Deviation: s", where s is the standard deviation of the sample. (Recall that the larger the standard deviation, the more variation is found in the data. More variation created larger confidence intervals for the mean. Here, more variation means a particular result is more likely the result of randomness, increasing the P-value.)

   In this test about Claim 1, what is the value of s that you should enter into Cell B2?

10. The third cell is labeled "Sample Size: n", where n is the size of the sample. What value should you type into Cell B3 to test Claim 1?

11. The last cell is labeled "Null Hypothesis μ_0=", where μ_0 is the value that is given – this is the value that you are comparing your population against in the claim. For Claim 1, what is the value for μ_0 that you should enter into Cell B5?

In cells B9, B10 and B11, we see three P-values. In this example, you should see 1.000, 0.000 and 0.000.

12. Which P-value should we use, and why?

13. If we use a significance level of 5%, what is the statistical conclusion, and what is the contextual conclusion of this hypothesis test?

Congratulations on completing your first full hypothesis test! Let's look at another claim, design the hypothesis test, run it, and interpret the results.

Claim 2: A majority of people who sleep less than 6.8 hours a night have been diagnosed with depression.

In order to test this claim, nearly 5000 people were surveyed about their sleep habits. Of these, 1000 people indicated they got less than 6.8 hours of sleep each night, and 525 of these people indicated that they had been diagnosed with depression.

14. Which of the following testable questions best addresses research Claim 2?

    (a) Is sleep an anti-depressant?

    (b) Is the average time an American who hasn't been diagnosed with depression spends sleeping greater than 6.8 hours a day?

    (c) Is the proportion of Americans who sleep less than 6.8 hours a day that have been diagnosed with depression greater than 0.50?

    (d) Is the average time an American who hasn't been diagnosed with depression spends sleeping greater than the average time an American who has been diagnosed with depression spends sleeping?

15. Write the null and alternative hypotheses.

The claim makes a statement about a *proportion* of *one group* of people (those who sleep less than 6.8 hours a night). Thus we need a 1-sample proportion test. (Look back to Problem 5 to ensure the Hyp. Test – 1 Proportion tab is indicated for this claim.)

When you open the `Hyp. Test -- 1 Proportion` tab, you should see three cells at the top that need to be filled in. We'll look at each cell, starting with the third cell.

16. Where it says "Null Hypothesis $p_0 =$", p_0 is the value that is given – this is the value that you are comparing your population against in the claim. For Claim 2, what is the value for p_0 that you should enter into Cell B4?

17. Where it says "Sample Size: n", n is the size of the sample. In this test about Claim 2, what is the value of n that you should enter into Cell B2?

18. Where is says "Sample Proportion: $\hat{p}$ ", $\hat{p}$ is the proportion of your sample that were diagnosed with depression. Which of the following should you type into Cell B1 to test Claim 2? (Hint – look at Cell C1, and remember that we want the sample proportion.)

   (a) 0.5

   (b) 525

   (c) =525/1000

   (d) =B4/1000

   If you haven't already done so, go ahead and fill in Cells B1, B2, and B4 with the corresponding answers from Problems 16–18.

   Once you have filled in your values, you should see these three P-values appear in cells B8, B9, and B10, respectively: 0.943, 0.057, and 0.114. We will only use one of these values to conclude our hypothesis test.

19. Which one do you think should be chosen? Why? What clues helped you pick the correct P-value?

20. The three P-values given are based on the three possible alternative hypotheses, so you should have chosen the P-value that matches your alternative hypothesis. In this case, your alternative hypothesis should have been $p > 0.5$, (or, in the notation of the Excel workbook, $p > p_0$), and that means your P-value is _____.

21. If we use a significance level of 5%, what is the statistical conclusion, and what is the contextual conclusion of this hypothesis test?

Check in with your instructor

Claim 3: People who include organic foods in their diets are less likely to have 2 or more colds in a year than those who do not.

   In order to test this claim, 1280 people were surveyed on their diets and health. Of the 627 people who include organic foods in their diets, 231 indicated that they had 2 or more colds in the past year. Of the remaining 653 people (i.e. those who do not include organic foods in their diets), 264 indicated that they had 2 or more colds in the past year.

22. Which of the following testable questions best addresses research Claim 3?

   (a) Is the proportion of people who include organic foods in their diet that had 2 or more colds in the past year less than the proportion of of people who do not include organic foods in their diet that had 2 or more colds in the past year?

(b) Is the average number of colds experienced in the past year by people who include organic foods in their diets less than the average number of colds experienced by people who do not include organic foods in their diets?

(c) Is the average number of colds experienced by people in the last year who include organic foods in their diet less than 2?

(d) Is the proportion of people who include organic foods in their diet that had 2 or more colds in the past year less than 0.5?

The correct choice uses a lot of words and makes a statement about the *proportion* (what proportion gets 2 or more colds?) of *two groups* of people (those use do, and do not, include organic food in their diet). We can simplify the wording of such statements by labeling each group.

For instance, let's let Group 1 be those who include organic food in their diet, and let Group 2 be those who do not include organic food in their diet. The correct testable question can be rewritten as

"Is the proportion of Group 1 people who had 2 or more colds in the past year less than the proportion of Group 2 people who had 2 or more colds in the past year?"

That question is still lengthy, but likely more readable.

The testable question references proportions for Group 1 and Group 2. It is common practice to denote these proportions as p_1 and p_2, respectively.

23. Write the null and alternative hypotheses using the notation described above.

As our claim refers to proportions of 2 groups of people, we need a 2-sample proportion test. (Look back to Problem 5 to ensure the Hyp. Test - 2 Proportion tab is indicated.)

When you open the Hyp. Test - 2 Proportion tab, you should see four cells at the top that need to be filled in.

24. Where is says "Sample Proportion: $\hat{p}_1$ ", $\hat{p}_1$ is the proportion of people from the sample who include organic foods in their diet that had 2 or more colds in the previous year. Which of the following should you type into Cell B2 to test Claim 2?

(a) 231

(b) =231/627

(c) =231/1280

(d) =264/653

Fill in the remaining cells, where n_1 is the number of people in Group 1, $\hat{p}_2$ is the proportion of people in Group 2 who got 2 or more colds in the previous year, and n_2 is the size of Group 2. You should see these three P-values appear in cells B8, B9, and B10, respectively: 0.094, 0.906, and 0.188. (If you don't see these values, check again the values you entered above.)

25. Which of the three values do we need? Why?

26. If we use a significance level of 10%, what is the statistical conclusion, and what is the contextual conclusion of this hypothesis test?

Review and Reflect

Take a moment to think back on this section. What were the main ideas? What did you find most interesting?

-

-

-

-

-

Hypothesis Testing Proportions and Means – Summary

- While there are many different types of hypothesis tests, we focus on tests for proportions, means, and independence. (The next section studies tests for independence.)

- Tests for proportion are often indicated by claims that use words such as "likely," "majority," "proportion" or "percentage."

- Tests for means are often indicated by the use of the word "average" in a claim.

- Tests for proportions and means can be 1-sample or 2-sample tests.

  - We use 1-sample tests when a statistic from one group is to be compared to a known value.

  - We use 2-sample tests when a statistic from two groups is to be compared to each other.

- Technology helps us quickly compute the P-values needed to draw conclusions from tests.

  - The user needs to know how the P-value(s) given relate to the null and alternate hypotheses.

  - When using the Excel Statistics Calculator.xslx file, the needed P-value is the one that aligns to the alternate hypothesis of the test.

Exercises 4.7

1. You are studying the benefit of a drug that is thought to increase the level of vitamin B12. You conduct an experiment and discover the mean levels of vitamin B12 in the sample who took the drug and the sample who took the placebo are: 320 pg/ml and 290 pg/ml, respectively. You want to know: Is the observed increase in B12 level statistically significant? Choose the best response.

   (a) Yes. The sample who used the drug had 320 pg/ml versus 290 pg/ml for those who did not.

   (b) Yes. The increase in B12 level was over 10% so the result is statistically significant.

   (c) It depends. The result is statistically significant if a large number of people participated in the study.

   (d) No. Although B12 level increased for those who took the drug, the increase was not large enough to be statistically significant.

   (e) It cannot be determined with the information provided. In order to conclude that the result is statistically significant, you need to know the p-value.

2. The Virginia Department of Transportation (VDOT) wanted to know if people were speeding (going faster than 70 mph) on I-81 between Lexington and Roanoke. VDOT recorded the speed of 100 vehicles using radar and found that the mean speed was 73 mph. Conducting a hypothesis test yields a p-value of 0.024. Which of the following is the best contextual conclusion of the result of this hypothesis test at the 5% significance level?

   (a) There is enough evidence to conclude that vehicles are going faster than 70 mph on I-81 between Lexington and Roanoke.

   (b) There is not enough evidence to conclude that vehicles are going faster than 70 mph on I-81 between Lexington and Roanoke.

   (c) Most cars go faster than 70 mph on I-81 between Lexington and Roanoke.

   (d) Most cars go slower than 70 mph on I-81 between Lexington and Roanoke.

Exercises 3 – 10 use the following information. A fertility clinic claims that their "YSORT procedure" will increase the likelihood of a couple having a baby girl. You may assume that the proportion of baby girls in the general population is 0.5. You want to test the claim that the YSORT method is effective.

3. What is a testable question for this problem?

4. In testing this claim, will you perform a 1-sample or 2-sample test?

5. In testing this claim, what statistics are used? Choose all that apply.

   (a) p = Proportion of baby girls

   (b) μ = Mean number of baby girls

   (c) p_1 = Proportion of baby girls

   (d) p_2 = Proportion of baby boys

   (e) p = Increase in proportion of baby girls

6. What is the correct statement of the null hypothesis?

   (a) $H_0 : p \leq 0.5$

   (b) $H_0 : p = 0.5$

   (c) $H_0 : p \geq 0.5$

7. What is the correct statement of the alternative hypothesis?

   (a) $H_1 : p < 0.5$

   (b) $H_1 : p = 0.5$

   (c) $H_1 : p > 0.5$

8. Suppose that 75 couples used the YSORT procedure and 46 of the couples had a baby girl. Using the statistics calculator in Excel, under the appropriate Hypothesis test tab, determine which P-value this test yields.

   (a) 0.972

   (b) 0.025

   (c) 0.057

9. If the significance level is 1%, what is your statistical conclusion based on the P-value you got in the previous question: Reject the null hypothesis, or Fail to reject the null hypothesis?

10. What is the contextual conclusion of this hypothesis test?

Exercises 11 – 18 consider the question "Do people who have a high school education earn less than those who complete a college degree?"

11. Write a testable question for this question.

12. In testing this question, how many samples are used?

   (a) 1-sample

   (b) 2-sample

   (c) It depends on how the experiment is conducted.

13. In testing this question, what statistic is used in the experiment?

   (a) μ = Mean income of college graduates

   (b) p = Proportion of college graduates who earn more than those with high school education

   (c) μ_1 = Mean income of high school graduates
       μ_2 = Mean income of college graduates

   (d) p_1 = Proportion of college graduates earning more than \$75,000/year
       p_2 = Proportion of high school graduates earning more than \$75,000/year

14. Let μ_1 = Mean income of high school graduates and μ_2 = Mean income of college graduates. What is the correct statement of the null hypothesis?

   (a) $H_0 : \mu_1 < \mu_2$

   (b) $H_0 : \mu_1 = \mu_2$

   (c) $H_0 : \mu_1 > \mu_2$

   (d) $H_0 : \mu_1 \leq \mu_2$

   (e) $H_0 : \mu_1 \geq \mu_2$

15. Let μ_1 = Mean income of high school graduates and μ_2 = Mean income of college graduates. What is the correct statement of the alternate hypothesis?

   (a) $H_1 : \mu_1 < \mu_2$

   (b) $H_1 : \mu_1 = \mu_2$

   (c) $H_1 : \mu_1 > \mu_2$

   (d) $H_1 : \mu_1 \leq \mu_2$

   (e) $H_1 : \mu_1 \geq \mu_2$

16. Suppose that the mean yearly salary of 10 college graduates is \$53,000 with a standard deviation of \$26,000 and the mean salary of 15 high school graduates is \$28,000 with a standard deviation of \$14,000. Using the hypothesis test calculator in Excel, which p-value does this test yield?

   (a) 0.9947

   (b) 0.0053

   (c) 0.0106

17. If the significance level is 5%, what is your statistical conclusion based on the p-value you got in the previous question: Reject the null hypothesis, or Fail to reject the null hypothesis?

18. What is the contextual conclusion of this hypothesis test?

4.8 Hypothesis Testing for Dependence

For this section, we will use the Excel workbook `MtM_Unit3b_CourseContent.xlsx`. You may also need to refer back to the instructions for creating a pivot table using Excel in Appendix A.

Looking for Dependence

Many professions are interested in answering questions of the form "Does Factor A influence Factor B?" This question is intentionally vague and broad, as it comes in many different forms. Here are some examples:

- Does your income level influence how likely you are to vote?

- Does your level of education influence your income level?

- Does being pregnant increase the likelihood of a woman buying moisturizing cream?

- Do different treatments for ankle sprain have different recovery times?

- (Pick two YouTube channels that you are subscribed to, calling them Channel A and Channel B.) Are subscribers to Channel A likely to enjoy watching Channel B?

The questions above can be answered using a *Test for Dependence*.[3] Two things are *independent* if they do not influence each other. For instance, suppose you are to guess if Alice likes to read Shakespeare, though you don't know anything about Alice. Then you are told she likes ice cream. Does that change how likely Alice is to enjoy reading Shakespeare? No. The two characteristics of "likes ice cream" and "likes Shakespeare" are likely independent – they do not influence each other.

For comparison, now consider that you are told that Alice is an English major in college. Does that change how likely Alice is to enjoy reading Shakespeare? Certainly. Of course, Alice *may not* enjoy reading Shakespeare, but it is probably safe to assume that many English majors do.

In a test for dependence, we start by assuming two factors *are independent* of each other, then look for evidence that they are actually *dependent*. Using the language of hypothesis testing, our null hypothesis will always effectively be "The two factors are independent." Therefore our alternate hypothesis will always be "The two factors are dependent."

To run a test for dependence, data will be collected and stored in a table, exactly in the same manner as when we looked at data with contingency tables and computed probabilities. Each row will relate to one particular factor, while each column will relate to the other factor.

Lie Detector Tests and Guilt: Dependent?

Think about the title above, and think about what *should* be the answer to that question. That is, *should* the results of a lie detector test be dependent on a person's guilt?

- Suppose they are independent. Then:

  - A person who is guilty is just as likely to pass a lie detector test as someone who is innocent.

  - Knowing that a person passed a lie detector test has no impact, at all, on determining whether or not the person is guilty or innocent.

- Suppose they are dependent. Then:

  - A person who is guilty has a different likelihood of passing a lie detector test as someone who is innocent. (Hopefully less.)

  - Knowing that a person passed a lie detector test helps determine whether or not a person is truly guilty or innocent.

---

[3]Most texts refer to this test as a Test for *Independence*. This convention isn't quite accurate, as we'll see that we assume *independence* with the null hypothesis and test for *dependence* with the alternate hypothesis.

Which of the above *should* be true? We *should* want lie detector tests to provide meaningful information about guilt and innocence. If these factors are independent, the test is useless. We *should* want dependence *in this example.*

Open the Excel spreadsheet HT_Dependence1 of MtM_Unit3b_CourseContent.xlsx. You should see a table just like the one below. (We used this dataset before; here we removed the Inconclusive results for simplicity.)

Observed Counts	Deceptive	Truthful	Total
Guilty	41	6	47
Innocent	27	18	45
Total	68	24	92

We will input the *expected counts* for each category in the adjacent table. These expected counts are based on the assumption that the row and column variables are independent of each other (this assumption will ultimately be our null hypothesis). To obtain these counts, we will take the probability that a particular category should occur and multiply it by the grand total of our sample.

Let's take the count of the "Guilty and Deceptive" category (cell I3) as an example. If we find the probability that a person is both guilty and found deceptive by the polygraph, we can use it to determine the number of people we should expect to fall into that category if the variable of guilt/innocence is independent of the outcome of the polygraph.

1. Use the contingency table to find the probability that a given person was identified as deceptive by the polygraph.

2. Now use the table to find the probability that a given person was found guilty.

You should have gotten 68/92 and 47/92, respectively. If we assume that a person's guilt/innocence is independent of the outcome of their polygraph, then the probability that a person is found guilty and declared deceptive by the polygraph is exactly the probability of being found guilty times the probability of being found deceptive by the polygraph. The assumption of independence is the only reason we can do this (otherwise, we would have to resort to conditional probabilities).

$$\text{Probability of Guilty and Deceptive} = \frac{47}{92} \times \frac{68}{92}.$$

Now that we know the probability of someone being guilty and deceptive, we simply multiply by the total number of subjects in our study to figure how many people we expect to be guilty and deceptive (assuming independence).

$$\text{Expected Count of Guilty and Deceptive} = \frac{47}{92} \times \frac{68}{92} \times 92 = \frac{(47)(68)}{92} = 34.74.$$

So we expect 34.74 people to be both guilty and deceptive. Notice that we can re-express this calculation using our contingency table:

$$\text{Expected Count of Guilty and Deceptive} = \frac{(\text{row 1 total})(\text{column 1 total})}{\text{total}}.$$

We can use the same idea for the rest of our table, i.e.

$$\text{Expected Count for a Cell} = \frac{(\text{row total})(\text{column total})}{\text{total}}.$$

3. Continue to fill in the entire table and record your answers in the table below. When you calculate your row and column totals, they should exactly match your observed totals.

Expected Counts	Deceptive	Truthful	Total
Guilty	34.74		
Innocent			
Total			

4. We can use Excel formulas to compute the value in each cell. As discussed above, the entry I3 can be computed as

$$\frac{(47)(68)}{92} = \text{E3*C5/E5}.$$

Can you think of how to use "$" signs appropriately to make this formula something you can click/drag into the other 3 cells of the table?

*** Check in with your instructor.

As mentioned before, the null and alternate hypotheses for a test for dependence will always have the same basic format. In our case, they are:

H_0: The row and column variables are independent. (I.e., lie detector test results are independent of guilt and innocence.)

H_1: The row and column variables are dependent. (I.e., lie detector test results are dependent of guilt and innocence.)

We now need a P-value. It is calculated with Excel's CHISQ.TEST function. This function needs to know where our two tables are located (without including the row/column totals). In a blank cell, type =CHISQ.TEST(C3:D4,I3:J4). (The notation "C3:D4" means "all cells in the rectangle with one corner at C3 and the other at D4." You can click/drag while typing this formula to create this range.)

5. Use Excel to calculate your P-value for the polygraph data.

6. With a 0.05 significance level, would you reject the null hypothesis?

7. Are the row and column variables independent for this example?

8. Does this align with what we thought "should" happen?

Conducting Tests for Dependence

As illustrated above, the Test for Dependence is a hypothesis test, just as we have been working with. It has a few requirements:

- The data must be randomly selected.

- The contingency table must use counts (not frequencies) in the cells.

- Every cell in the expected counts table must have at least a value of 5 or higher.

If all of these conditions are met, then we will be able to determine if the row variables and the column variables are dependent (the variables do influence each other).

We will also need to use the significance value and the P-value (found through an Excel command) to determine the conclusion of our test. The Null and Alternative Hypotheses for this test are always the same, and are as follows:

H_0: The row and column variables are independent.
H_1: The row and column variables are dependent.

Although the variables in the rows and columns change depending on the contingency table, the hypotheses remain the same. It is good, though, to think through what each statement means in context of the given problem.

To calculate the P-value, we will be using the CHISQ.TEST command in Excel. To use this command, you need to already have your contingency table (observed counts) and have calculated your expected count table. The CHISQ.TEST command requires two inputs, all the cell data from your observed counts except the totals, and all the cell data from your expected counts except the totals. The output is the P-value, which is to be compared against the significance level.

Important: If P is lower than the significance level, we reject the null hypothesis and conclude the two factors are dependent.

If P is not lower than the significance level, we *fail to reject* the null hypothesis. We do not *prove* they are independent, just as a court case does not prove innocence. Rather, we have just failed to show the factors are dependent. This is why it is more accurate to call this a "Test for Dependence" than a "Test for Independence." We assume independence, then look for evidence of dependence.

The US Voter Data - Are Rally Attendance and Voting Dependent?

Political scientists, such as some faculty in the Department of International Studies and Political Science here at VMI, use information from voters to understand what factor(s) determine whether a voter will actually vote in an election.

We will be working with United States voter data from the 2012 election to try and determine which factors correlate with voter participation.

Open the Excel spreadsheet `HT_VoterData` in `MtM_Unit3b_CourseContent.xlsx`, which contains information collected from 3895 US voters. Each row (after the first) represents data collected on an individual voter. Look at the labels in the first row. The meanings of some of the labels are fairly evident though others are not; it is probably not clear what the numbers in the table indicate. (We will get to that soon.)

A political scientist would like to look at the following outcomes: attend rallies, work campaign, and turnout. Table 4.4 describes the meanings of the numbers found in those columns.

Table 4.4: Outcomes

Outcomes	Description
attend rallies	0 if the voter did not attend and
	1 if the voter attended a rally
work campaign	0 if the voter did not work on a campaign and
	1 if the voter worked on a campaign
turnout	0 if the person did not vote and
	1 if the person voted

We will go through the steps of testing whether or not Rally Attendance is dependent of Voting (Turnout).

9. In `HT_VoterData`, Insert a PivotTable in some blank cells.

   (a) Drag "attend_rallies" down to the ROWS box in the PivotTable Fields menu.

   (b) Drag "turnout" into the COLUMNS box in the same menu.

   (c) Drag "turnout" into the VALUES box in the same menu. Make sure that Value Field setting is "Count of turnout".

   You should have created a PivotTable identical to the one shown in Figure 4.8.1.

Figure 4.8.1: PivotTable for Voter Data (initial)

Count of turnout	Column Labels			
Row Labels		0	1	(blank)	Grand Total
0		1083	4058		5141
1		22	323		345
(blank)		1	23		24
Grand Total		1106	4404		5510

   (d) The data collectors were not always able to ascertain if a person did or didn't vote, or did or didn't attend a rally. So some entries are blank, as indicated by the third row and third column. We want to remove those rows/columns. To do so, click on the icon next to "Row Labels" to see the menu shown in Figure 4.8.2.

Figure 4.8.2: PivotTable for Voter Data (remove blank entries)

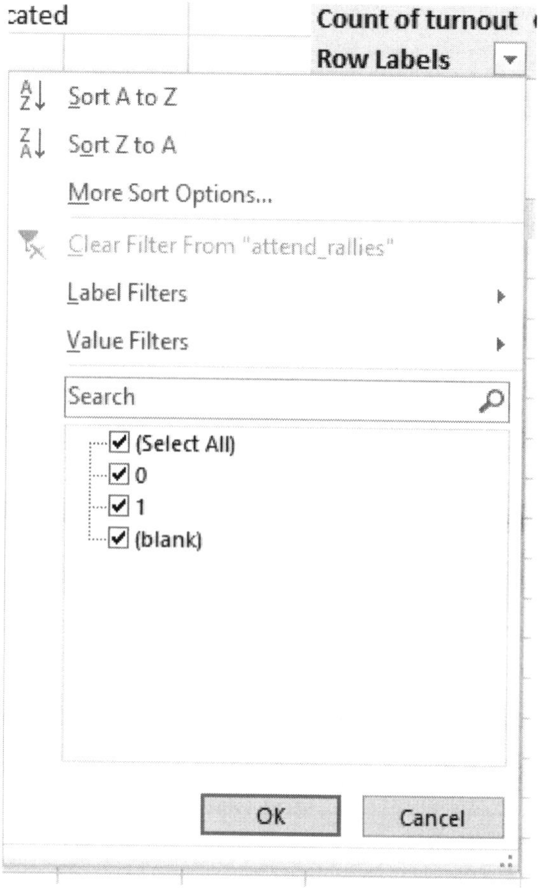

Un-check the box next to "(blank)". Then do the same thing for the columns by clicking on the icon next to "Column Labels."

Your PivotTable should look like the one shown at top of Figure 4.8.3.

Figure 4.8.3: PivotTable for Voter Data (final)

Count of turnout	Column Labels		
Row Labels	0	1	Grand Total
0	1083	4058	5141
1	22	323	345
Grand Total	1105	4381	5486
	1035.509479	4105.5	
	69.49052133	275.51	

(e) Create the Expected Values table needed for the dependence test. The computed values are shown in Figure 4.8.3, at bottom.

(f) Use CHISQ.TEST to compute the *P*-value. You should see something similar to "4.53E-11". This is Excel's way of writing "4.53×10^{-11}," which is 0.0000000000453. (A *very* small number.)

(g) Can we conclude that Attending Rallies and Voting are dependent of each other? (Does this make common sense?)

*** **Check in with your instructor.**

This table explains what each number means in the US Voter Data dataset.

Table 4.5: Factors

Factors	Description
Incumbent	0 for non-incumbent candidate and 1 if the candidate is currently holding the position
Economy eval	1 if voter thinks the economy is worse, 2 for stayed the same and 3 for better
Income	1 for the 0-16th percentile, 2 for 17-33rd, 3 for 34-67th, 4 for 68-95th and 5 for 96-100th percentile
Influence votes	0 if the voter did not try to influence other votes and 1 if they tried to influence other votes
Ideology	1 for extremely liberal, 2 for liberal, 3 for slightly liberal, 4 for the middle, 5 for slightly conservative, 6 for conservative, 7 for extremely conservative
Party ID	1 for democrats, 2 for independents and 3 for republicans
Party strength	1 for completely independent, 2 for leaning independent, 3 for weakly tied to a party and 4 for strongly tied to a party
Education	1 for less than 8th grade, 2 for high school, 3 for some college and 4 for college or advanced degree
Politics discussed	0 for not discussing politics and 1 for discussing politics
Age	1 ages 17-24, 2 for 25-34, 3 for 35-44, 4 for 45-54, 5 for 55-64, 6 for 65-74, 7 for 75 or older
Female	0 for male and 1 for female
Politics complicated	0 if the voter thinks politics are not complicated and 1 if the voter thinks it is complicated

Your Own Data Analysis: Contingency Tables for the Voter Data

You will be assigned one of the factors shown in Table 4.5. You are to:

- Make three separate contingency tables (pivot tables) using the data for the given factor and the three factors of "attend rallies", "work campaign", and "turnout";

- Copy your tables into the spreadsheet HT_Dependence2 of MtM_Unit3b_CourseContent.xlsx. There are pre-made, colored tables for you to use. Depending on the number of categories for your factor, you may need to remove some rows in each table.

- **Important Note:** When you copy the data over to the US Voter tab, **do not** include the "(blank)" category!

10. As described above, create the contingency table that uses your factor and Attended Rallies.

11. As described above, create the contingency table that uses your factor and Worked Campaigns.

12. As described above, create the contingency table that uses your factor and Turnout.

*** Check in with your instructor before moving on to the next questions.

Once you have the Observed contingency tables, run the Test for Dependence for each outcome and determine if your factor was influential to rally attendance, working with the campaigns and/or voting.

- Complete each Expected contingency table.

- Use Excel to calculate your *P*-value for each outcome.

- With a 5% significance level, would you reject the null hypothesis?

- Are the row and column variables independent for this example?

- How would you present your conclusion to a political scientists? (Does your factor influence one or more of the outcomes?)

***Check in with your instructor.

Review and Reflect

Take a moment to think back on this section. What were the main ideas? What did you find most interesting?

-

-

-

-

-

Hypothesis Testing For Dependence – Summary

- If two factors are related, in that knowledge of one factor informs knowledge about the second factor, we say the factors are *dependent*. Otherwise, we say the factors are *independent*.

- A "Test for Dependence" is a hypothesis test relating to the dependence/independence of two factors.
    - The null hypothesis is always that the factors are independent.
    - The alternate hypothesis is always that the factors are dependent.
    - As we either reject the null hypothesis or fail to reject the null hypothesis, we either reject independence (i.e., show factors are dependent) or fail to reject independence. That is, we don't *prove* independence, just fail to show factors aren't independent.

- We use the CHISQ.TEST command in Excel to obtain a *P*-value for a hypothesis test.
    - Create a frequency (or, contingency) table of your observed data, where the rows of the table have characteristics of one factor and the columns have characteristics of the other. A pivot table may be useful in making this table.
    - Create another table with the expected counts using the formula

$$\text{Expected Count for a Cell} = \frac{(\text{row total})(\text{column total})}{\text{total}}.$$

    - The formula "=CHISQ.TEST(*observed range,expected range*)" returns a *P*-value that can be compared against a significance level.

Exercises 4.8

Exercises 1 – 7 use the 2012 study by Bruce Jancin from the Internal Medicine Journal on the treatment of a particular type of foot stress fracture. The contingency table is as follows.

	Success	Failure	Total
Surgery	54	12	66
Weight-Bearing Cast	41	51	92
Non-Weight-Bearing Cast (6 weeks)	70	3	73
Non- Weight-Bearing Cast (less than 6 weeks)	17	5	22
Total	182	71	253

1. Find the Expected Frequency for success with non-weight-bearing cast (6 weeks).

   (a) 0.7194

   (b) 52.5138

   (c) 70

   (d) 177.1

2. We would like to run a test for dependence on the treatment types and outcomes. Determine the null hypothesis.

   (a) H_0 : The success of the treatment is independent of the type of treatment.

   (b) H_0 : The success of the treatment is dependent of the type of treatment.

   (c) The test for independence is not a hypothesis test.

3. We would like to run a test for dependence on the treatment types and outcomes. Determine the alternate hypothesis.

   (a) H_1: The success of the treatment is independent of the type of treatment.

   (b) H_1: The success of the treatment is dependent of the type of treatment.

   (c) The test for independence is not a hypothesis test.

4. What would it mean for the success of the treatment to be independent of the treatment type?

   (a) A patient is just as likely to have a successful recovery regardless of whether they had surgery, wore a weight bearing cast, etc.

   (b) A patient is more likely to have a successful recovery through some treatments than others.

   (c) The types of treatments do not affect each other.

5. Create the table of expected frequency counts.

6. A test for dependence was performed on 2012 Internal Medicine Journal stress fracture study. The P-value is 1.296E-12. What does mean?

   (a) It is an error code in Excel; something went wrong.

   (b) The minus sign means it's a very small number; it is Excel's way of writing 1.296×10^{-12}, or 0.000000000001296.

   (c) It is a very large number; it is Excel's way of writing 1.296×10^{12}, or 1,296,000,000,000.

7. A test for dependence was performed on 2012 Internal Medicine Journal stress fracture study. The P-value is 1.296E-12. Using a 0.05 significance level, what would the conclusion be?

(a) We fail to reject the null hypothesis. The success is independent of the treatment type.

(b) We fail to reject the null hypothesis. The success is dependent on the treatment type.

(c) We reject the null hypothesis. The success is independent of the treatment type.

(d) We reject the null hypothesis. The success is dependent on the treatment type.

(e) The test was inconclusive.

4.9 Hypothesis Testing Review

Hypothesis testing is an important tool when making decisions in situations where randomness or uncertainty are present. As we've covered the topic over the past four sections, a review is in order to help put all the pieces together.

At the heart of hypothesis testing is the following scenario: you observe an event and wonder "Is what I observed the result of random chance, or is something more significant going on?"

To answer that question, we need to find the probability that the event happened from chance. Once that probability is found (we use `Statistics Calculator.xlsx`), we have to decide: is that probability low enough for us to accept? If it is, we decide something other than randomness happened. (We *reject the null* and accept the alternate hypothesis.) If not, we assume what we saw was just randomness (and we *fail to reject the null*).

The following problems will help review all the steps involved.

1. You are interested in testing the claim that residents of Virginia spend more time outside than residents of North Carolina. You survey residents from both states, and find that Virginians spend, on average, 9.8 hours outside per week with a standard deviation of 1.2 hours, while North Carolinians spend an average of 9.6 hours per week with a standard deviation of 1.4 hours.

    (a) Which hypothesis test would best help address this scenario?

        i. 1-sample proportion
        ii. 2-sample proportion
        iii. 1-sample mean
        iv. 2-sample mean
        v. Test for dependence

    (b) After running the hypothesis test, the *P*-value you obtain indicates that you fail to reject the null hypothesis. In this case, what is the contextual conclusion?

        i. Virginians spend less than 9.8 hours outside per week.
        ii. Virginians do not spend more time outside than North Carolinians.
        iii. Virginians spend more time outside than North Carolinians.
        iv. There is not enough evidence to suggest that the time spent outside by North Carolinians depends on the amount of time spent outside by Virginians.
        v. There is not enough evidence to suggest that Virginians spend more time outside than North Carolinians.

2. Suppose that you want to conduct a study aimed at determining whether or not a person's sports preference depends on their gender. To this end, you survey 691 people, asking them to indicate their gender (male or female) and their sports preference (football, soccer, basketball, tennis, volleyball, and hockey).

    (a) Which hypothesis test would you run on this data?

        (i) 1-sample proportion
        (ii) 2-sample proportion
        (iii) 1-sample mean
        (iv) 2-sample mean
        (v) Test for dependence

    (b) After running the hypothesis test, the *P*-value you obtain indicates that you should reject the null hypothesis. In this case, what is the contextual conclusion?

        i. The proportion of males who like football is greater than 0.6.
        ii. The proportion of males who like soccer is less than the proportion of females who like soccer.
        iii. The average number of people who like tennis is less than 691.
        iv. Sports preferences depend on gender.
        v. There is not enough evidence to suggest that sports preferences depend on gender.

3. To investigate preferred modes of communication, you decide to survey people on whether they prefer talking on the phone or texting.

   (a) Which hypothesis test would you run to test the claim that a majority of people prefer texting over speaking over the phone?

      i. 1-sample proportion
      ii. 2-sample proportion
      iii. 1-sample mean
      iv. 2-sample mean
      v. Test for dependence

   (b) After running the hypothesis test, the P-value you obtain indicates that you should reject the null hypothesis. In this case, what is the contextual conclusion?

      i. There is sufficient evidence to support the claim that the proportion of people who prefer texting is greater than 0.5.
      ii. The proportion of people who prefer texting is greater than the proportion of people who prefer talking on the phone.
      iii. There is sufficient evidence to support the claim that the proportion of people who prefer texting is the same or less than the proportion of people who prefer talking on the phone.
      iv. There is not enough evidence to suggest that the number of people who prefer texting is less than the proportion of people who prefer talking on the phone.
      v. People who prefer texting are independent of people who prefer speaking on the phone.

4. A research group conducted a study looking for a connection between gender and preferences in treatments for quitting smoking. The following data was collected as part of the study:

	Patch	Gum	E-Cigarette	Total
Men	55	71	32	158
Women	65	52	45	162
Total	120	123	77	320

   (a) What type of hypothesis test best fits this scenario?

      i. 1-sample proportion
      ii. 2-sample proportion
      iii. 1-sample mean
      iv. 2-sample mean
      v. Test for dependence

   (b) Write down the null and alternative hypotheses for this scenario using proper statistical notation.

      H_0 :

      H_1 :

   (c) Use Excel to determine the P-value for this trial.

   (d) What is the statistical conclusion for this trial using a 5% significance level?

   (e) What is the contextual conclusion for this trial?

5. When 40 people used a weight loss program for one year, their mean weight loss was 3.0 pounds and the standard deviation was 8.9 pounds. Does this sample indicate the weight loss program is effective? Use a 5% significance level to test the claim that the average weight loss is greater than 0.0 pounds.

   (a) What type of hypothesis test best fits this scenario?

       i. 1-sample proportion

       ii. 2-sample proportion

       iii. 1-sample mean

       iv. 2-sample mean

       v. Test for dependence

   (b) Write down the null and alternative hypotheses for this scenario using proper statistical notation.

   H_0 :

   H_1 :

   (c) Use Statistics Calculator.xlsx to determine the P-value for this trial.

   (d) What is the statistical conclusion for this trial?

   (e) What is the contextual conclusion for this trial?

6. During quality assurance testing, a cell phone manufacturer randomly selects 300 phones from a shipment and tests them for defects. If testing suggests that more than 10% of the shipment is defective, then that batch of phones is not shipped. Within this particular sample, 37 phones are found to be defective.

   (a) What type of hypothesis test best fits this scenario?

       i. 1-sample proportion

       ii. 2-sample proportion

       iii. 1-sample mean

       iv. 2-sample mean

       v. Test for dependence

   (b) Write down the null and alternative hypotheses for this scenario using proper statistical notation.

   H_0 :

   H_1 :

   (c) Use the Statistics Calculator/Excel to determine the P-value for this test.

(d) If we use a 5% significance level, what is the statistical conclusion for this test?

(e) What is the contextual conclusion for this trial at the 5% significance level?

(f) What if, during testing, we used a 10% significance level? What is the statistical conclusion?

(g) What is the contextual conclusion at the 10% significance level?

(h) If you were the quality assurance tester, which significance level would you choose? Why did you choose this significance level?

*** **Check in with your instructor.**

Appendix A

Creating a Frequency Table With Excel

These videos may be of use, in addition to the instructions that follow.

- https://www.gcflearnfree.org/excel2016/intro-to-pivottables/1/

- https://www.gcflearnfree.org/excel2016/doing-more-with-pivottables/1/

Open the Excel worksheet VS_VFT Data of the workbook MtM_Unit2_CourseContent.xlsx, which contains VMI Fitness Test (VFT) data for over 1500 Cadets.

Frequency Table

1. Create a new worksheet

   - Insert a new worksheet and change the name to Frequency Table.
   - Return to the ST_VFT Data worksheet.

2. Create a Pivot Table

   - Go to the ST_VFT Data worksheet and click any cell in it.
   - Click on the **Insert>Pivot Table** menu item.
   - The **Create Pivot Table** window will pop up.
     - Click on the **Existing Worksheet** radio button.
     - Click on the tab of the Frequency Table worksheet you just created.
     - Click on the top left cell in the Frequency Table worksheet.
     - Click **OK**.

3. Format the Pivot Table to Create a Frequency Table

   This step formats the Pivot Table on the Frequency Table worksheet.

   - Find the list of **Pivot Table Fields** (top right).
   - Click on **Height**.
   - Drag **Height** to the rows section.
   - A list of **Row Labels** appears in the top left of the worksheet and all of the values of heights are listed.
   - Right click on any of the height values under **Row Labels**.
   - Click **Group** and the **Grouping Dialog Box** appears and provides three options to adjust the classes (bins). Start by entering these values:
     - Starting At: 57

-   Ending At: 81
-   By: 5

-   Click **OK**.

There are now 5 rows in the pivot table, which should look something like this:

Row Labels
57-61
62-66
67-71
72-76
77-81
Grand Total

-   Next you need to create the count of heights for each row. Return to the **Pivot Table Fields** on the top right (if this sidebar is not present, right click on your pivot table and select **Show Field Lists**).

-   Note: If the Pivot Table Fields window disappeared click on any cell underneath Row Labels in the top left corner of the spreadsheet.

-   Select **Height** and drag it down to the Σ **Values** section. If **Sum of Height** or **Count of Height** is already in this section, you may skip this step.

-   Left click on **Sum of Height** or **Count of Height** and select **Value Field Settings**. . . and the **Value Field Settings** dialog box appears.

-   Click on the **Summarize Values Field By** tab and make sure the **Count** field is selected in the list box.

-   In the **Custom Name** entry box type: **Frequency**.

-   Click **OK**.

The final product should look like this:

Row Labels	Frequency
57-61	26
62-66	266
67-71	794
72-76	422
77-81	14
Grand Total	1522

Creating a Relative Frequency Table

This step is a continuation of Steps 1 to 3. Complete them first.

4. Creating a Relative Frequency Table

-   Find the list of **Pivot Table Fields** (top right).

-   Select **Height** and drag it down to the Σ **Values** section.

-   Left click on **Count of Height** and select **Value Field Settings**. . . and the **Value Field Settings** dialog box appears.

-   Click on the **Summarize Values Field By** tab and select **Count** in the list box.

-   In the **Custom Name** entry box type: **Relative Frequency**.

-   Click on the **Show Values As** tab and select **% of Column Total** in the drop down box.

-   Click **OK**.

The final product should look like this:

Row Labels	Frequency	Relative Frequency
57-61	26	1.71%
62-66	266	17.48%
67-71	794	52.17%
72-76	422	27.73%
77-81	14	0.92%
Grand Total	1522	100.00%

Creating a Relative Frequency Table by Gender

This step is a continuation of Steps 1 to 4. Complete them first.

5. Creating a Relative Frequency Table by Gender

- Find the list of **Pivot Table Fields** (top right).
- Select **Gender** and drag it down to the top of the list in the **Columns** section.

The final product should look like this:

	Column Labels					
	F		M		Total Frequency	Total Relative Frequency
Row Labels	Frequency	Relative Frequency	Frequency	Relative Frequency		
57-61	24	14.72%	2	0.15%	26	1.71%
62-66	98	60.12%	168	12.36%	266	17.48%
67-71	39	23.93%	755	55.56%	794	52.17%
72-76	2	1.23%	420	30.91%	422	27.73%
77-81		0.00%	14	1.03%	14	0.92%
Grand Total	163	100.00%	1359	100.00%	1522	100.00%

Appendix B

Creating a Histogram Using Excel

There are many excellent video tutorials showing you how to create Pivot Tables and Pivot Charts using Excel. If you want further help, find several offerings and select one. This video is a good example of what is available: `https://www.youtube.com/watch?v=9NUjHBNWe9M`.

Note that an Excel Pivot Chart is also a histogram but with some difference in formatting the x-axis. There is also an option in Excel to directly create a histogram using **Insert**, and selecting the icon for a histogram. Choose whichever option is easier for you. This document uses the Create Pivot Table & Pivot Chart option because it closely follows the steps used in the previous lesson to create a frequency table.

Open the Excel worksheet VS_VFT Data of the workbook MtM_Unit2_CourseContent.xlsx, which contains VMI Fitness Test (VFT) data for over 1500 Cadets.

1. Create a new worksheet.

    - Insert a new worksheet and change the name to Histogram.
    - Return to the ST_VFT Data worksheet.

2. Create a Pivot Table & Pivot Chart

    - Go to the ST_VFT Data worksheet and click any cell in it.
    - Click on the **Insert>Pivot Chart** (the drop down menu) and select **Pivot Chart & Pivot Table**.
    - The **Create Pivot Table** window will pop up.
        - Click on the **Existing Worksheet** radio button.
        - Click on the tab of the Histogram worksheet you just created.
        - Click on the top left cell in the Histogram worksheet.
        - Click **OK**.
        - A Pivot Table should appear on the left and a Chart should appear in the middle,

3. Formatting the Pivot Table & Pivot Chart The next step is formatting the Pivot Table on the Histogram worksheet.

    - Find the list of **Pivot Table Fields** (top right), clicking on a cell in the Pivot Table on the left if necessary.
    - Click and Drag **Height** to the **Rows** or **Axis (Categories)** section at the bottom.
    - A list of **Row Labels** appears in the top left of the worksheet and all of the values of heights are listed.
    - Right click on any of the height values under **Row Labels**.
    - Click **Group** and the **Grouping Dialog Box** appears and provides three options to adjust the classes (bins). Start by entering these values:
        - Starting At: 57

    - Ending At: 81
    - By: 5.
  - Click **OK**.
  - There are now 5 rows in the pivot table:
    Row Labels
    57-61
    62-66
    67-71
    72-76
    77-81
    Grand Total
  - Next you need to create the count of heights for each row. Return to the **Pivot Table Fields** on the top right.
  - Select **Height** and drag it down to the Σ **Values** section. If **Sum of Height** or **Count of Height** is already in this section, you may skip this step.
  - If the field in the Σ **Values** section is not already formatted to **Count of Height**, Left click and select **Value Field Settings**. . . and the **Value Field Settings** dialog box appears. Then select the **Summarize Values Field By** tab and select **Count** in the list box (and click **OK**).

Excel updates the Pivot Table (frequency table) in the top left of the spreadsheet and at the same time creates a Pivot Chart (histogram) in the center of the spreadsheet. The final product should look like this:

Pivot Table

Row Labels	Count of Height
57-61	26
62-66	266
67-71	794
72-76	422
77-81	14
Grand Total	**1522**

Pivot Chart

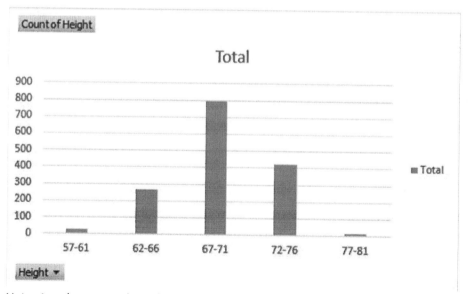

Note: Any changes made to the frequency table are automatically incorporated into the histogram.

4. Make the pivot chart look like a histogram for a final version.

   (a) Right click on the **Height** button in the lower left corner of the histogram and select **Hide All Field Buttons on Chart**. It should look like this now:

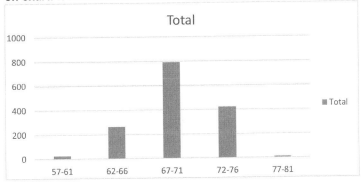

   (b) Right click on any histogram bar and select **Format Data Series**. A panel on the right side of the window displays options. Adjust the **Gap Width** to 5%. In general, histogram bars should either touch (if Gap Width is zero) or have a very small gap between them.

   (c) Click on the title text box in the top center and change 'Total' to 'Distribution of Cadet Height'.

   (d) Click in the middle of the chart and then click on the + sign on the top right. A Chart Elements list appears. Check 'Axis Titles' and 'Data Labels', and uncheck 'Legend'. You may also do this by clicking on the chart, selecting **Design** in the green ribbon at the top of the Excel window, and clicking on **Add Chart Element**. This tool will allow you to add and remove legends, axis titles, etc.

   (e) Edit the default values for the horizontal and vertical axis titles.

Your histogram should look like this:

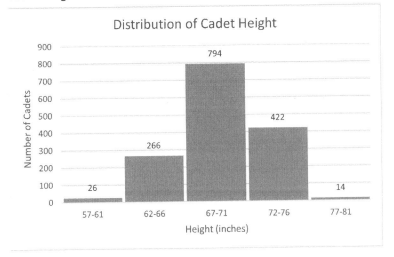

Appendix C

Using Pivot Tables to Calculate Statistics

When one has a large set of data, one may be interested in computing statistics on certain subcategories of the data. For instance, one may have a large data set containing people's annual salary, education level, and home state. One might be interested in the mean salary by state, or the median salary by education level.

    The following steps show the principles of easily computing such statistics using Pivot Tables in Excel, by finding the mean (average) and standard deviations of cadet heights, by gender.

1. Open the VS_VFT Data worksheet of the workbook MtM_Unit2_CourseContent.xlsx,

2. Create a new worksheet

   - Insert a new worksheet and change the name to **Pivot Table**.
   - Return to the VS_VFT Data worksheet.

3. Create a Pivot Table

   - Select all of the columns in the table.
   - Click on the **Insert>Pivot Table** menu item.
   - The **Create Pivot Table** window will pop up.
   - Click on the **Existing Worksheet** radio button.
   - Click on the tab of the **Pivot Table** worksheet you just created.
   - Click on the top left cell in the Pivot Table worksheet
   - Click **OK**.

4. Format the Pivot Table to Calculate Mean & Standard Deviation of Height by Gender

   - Set up the table to give separate Male and Female rows.
     - Find the list of **Pivot Table Fields** (top right).
     - Click on **Gender**.
     - Drag **Gender** to the **Rows** section.
     - A list of **Row Labels** appears in the top left of the worksheet and the values **F** and **M** are listed.
   - Find the average height by gender.
     - Return to the **Pivot Table Fields** on the top right.
     - Select **Height** and drag it down to the Σ Values section.
     - Left click on **Height** and select **Value Field Settings...**, and the **Value Field Settings** dialog box appears.
     - Click on the **Summarize Values Field By** tab and select **Average** in the list box.
     - In the **Custom Name** entry box type: Mean.

– Click **OK**.

The pivot table should look like this:

Row Labels	Mean
F	64.54601227
M	69.99852833
Grand Total	69.41458607

- The final step is finding the standard deviation of height by gender.
    - Return to the **Pivot Table Fields** on the top right.
    - Select **Height** and drag it down to the Σ Values section.
    - Left click on **Height** and select **Value Field Settings...**, and the **Value Field Settings** dialog box appears.
    - Click on the **Summarize Values Field By** tab and select **StdDev** in the list box.
    - In the **Custom Name** entry box type: **Standard Deviation**
    - Click **OK**.

The pivot table should now look like this:

Row Labels	Mean	Standard Deviation
F	64.54601227	2.946440527
M	69.99852833	2.988194378
Grand Total	69.41458607	3.426642356

Appendix D

BATtleship Slopes

Turn the page upside down to read.

Slope #1, Total: 55 bats

	A	B	C	D	E	F	G	H	I	J
1	0	0	1	1	1	0	0	0	0	0
2	0	0	0	2	2	1	2	0	1	0
3	0	1	0	2	1	2	0	1	0	1
4	1	0	1	0	2	1	1	0	0	0
5	0	0	1	1	0	2	1	2	0	0
6	0	0	0	2	1	0	1	1	1	0
7	0	0	1	0	0	2	0	0	0	1
8	0	0	1	0	1	0	2	1	0	0
9	1	1	0	0	2	1	1	0	0	0
10	0	0	1	0	1	0	0	1	0	0

Slope #2, Total: 400 bats

	A	B	C	D	E	F	G	H	I	J
1	200	1	0	1	2	0	0	1	1	0
2	0	0	0	1	0	2	0	0	1	0
3	0	1	0	0	0	0	1	1	0	1
4	1	0	1	1	0	2	0	0	1	0
5	0	0	0	0	1	1	0	1	1	0
6	0	1	0	1	0	2	2	0	0	100
7	0	1	0	0	2	0	0	0	1	1
8	1	0	0	1	2	0	2	1	0	0
9	0	1	0	1	0	2	0	1	0	0
10	50	0	0	0	0	1	0	0	1	1

Appendix E

Solutions to Questions Within the Text

Chapter 1

Section 1.3: Cultural Trip Worksheet

1. (a) 1950

   (b) 2793.75 (though the answer may be rounded if your cell is too narrow)

   (c) (though the answer may be rounded if your cell is too narrow)

   (d) 13*150 (the cell shows exactly what you typed)

2. (a) food cost for group in USD

   (b) cost per person in ¥

   (c) total group cost in ¥

   (d) nothing

3. =B1 * B10 (or = 13 * 150)

4. (b)

5. = B2 * B6

6. = B2 * B9

7. (c)

8. =13*B9

9. (a)

10. =13*D15

11. Well. . . were you correct?

12. (a) =B2 * B6

    (b) =$B$2 * $B8

    (c) = B2* B9

13. The dollar-sign $ indicates that that particular part of the reference won't change when copy/pasted into another formula. That reference is *absolute* - it is always the same.

15. The numbers in the table stay the same, but the formula for C9 in the formula bar changes to an absolute reference.

16. Enter = $B$1 * $B6 into cell B15 and drag the formula down the column. Enter =$B$2 * $B15 into cell C15 and drag the formula down the column.

17. • Cell B19: =SUM(B15:B18)

    • Cell C10: =$B$2*SUM(B6:B9)

    • Cell C11: =$B$1*SUM(C6:C9)

    • Cell C19: =SUM(C15:C18)

18. Cost percentages can be computed using either the individual costs in Table A or in Table B; the results will be the same.

    • Using Table A, in cell B22 use =B6/$B$10, then drag this formula down to B25.

    • Using Table B, in cell B22 use =B15/$B$19, then drag this formula down to B25.

19. In the pie chart, three of the sections are too close in size to determine their relative size. While pie charts are popular, this is a significant shortcoming.

    The line graph is more appropriate when quantities change over time, unlike here. The lines imply that there are costs between each category, which is not the case.

    By contrast, it's easy to read and compare categories in the bar chart. The bar chart is best in this case.

Chapter 2

Section 2.1: Creating Data – Simulating Emigration

3. We expect about half of the 10 rolled M&Ms to land "m" side up. So the population model starts at 60, then goes to 55, 50, etc. The Excel formula =C2-5*A2 in cell D2 can be dragged down to D11 to accomplish this.

4. If the initial population was 60 and in each iteration the population is reduced by 5, then the data in the **Model** column can be described by the equation $y = 60 - 5x$, where x is the number of iterations. This can be accomplished by entering =$C$2-5*A2 in cell D2 and dragging this formula down to D12.

7. Answers will vary depending on the randomness of the rolled M&Ms. Most people find the model and the data appear to be very similar.

8. The data most likely looks like (b). The M&M population decreases at a rate of about 5.

11. If you started with 4 M&Ms, and on each turn half of the 6 rolled M&Ms landed "M" side up, then in each iteration you would add 3 M&Ms to the population. So the population would start at 4, then go to 7, 10, etc.

12. If the initial population was 4 and in each iteration the population increases by 3, then the data in the **Model** column can be described by the equation $y = 4 + 3x$, where x is the number of iterations. This can be accomplished by entering =$C$2+3*A2 in cell D2 and dragging this formula down to D12.

15. Answers will vary depending on the randomness of the rolled M&Ms. Most people find the model and the data appear to be very similar.

16. The data most likely looks like (a). The M&M population increases at a rate of about 3.

Section 2.1: Making a Model Using a Linear Trendline

18. (a) Equations will vary depending on the randomness of the rolled M&Ms. The numbers in the equation will likely be close to the numbers in the **Model** equation created earlier.

    (b) The variable x represents the Iteration number. The variable y represents the Current Population, measured in "number of M&Ms."

    (c) The m-value will vary depending on the number of M&Ms rolled per turn. It should be about half the number of M&Ms rolled per turn. If you rolled 10 M&Ms, the m-value is likely near 5. The units of m are "number of M&Ms per iteration."

    The b-value should be near the number of M&Ms you started with in Iteration 0. The units of b are "number of M&Ms."

19. The m-value is the slope of the line. It describes how quickly the line rises or falls. The b-value is called the "y-intercept", and indicates where the line crosses the y-axis.

20. The m coefficient tells us how quickly the M&M population grows or declines; how much the population grows/declines per iteration. The b coefficient approximates what the M&M population was at iteration 0.

21. Answers will vary depending the actual trendline determined by the data. In general, $x = 15$ and find the predicted population.

    It is possible, if the m-value is negative, that the predicted population is negative. Since negative populations are not possible, that simply means the predicted population is 0.

22. While each trendline and data set are different, the will very, very likely be, "No."

23. Answers will vary depending on the data set. It is very likely that R^2 is near 1.

24. Given a data set with x- and y-values, one expects the y-values to vary, or change. The R^2-value explains "What proportion of the change seen in the y-values is explained by the trendline?" As an example, if we find that $R^2 = 0.8$, then the trendline explains 80% of the change seen in the y-values.

25. While answers will vary, in this example it is very likely that R^2 is near 1. That is, the trendline will explain nearly 100% of the change in the y-values.

26. We assume that the color of the candy does not affect its chances of landing "m" side up. This is essentially stated earlier when we said "we assume that each M&M has a 50% chance of landing "m"-side up."

Section 2.2: Creating Data – Simulating Birth

8. The correct answer is likely (c). The graph is increasing, and it likely started relatively flat and got steeper with each iteration.

Section 2.2: Creating Data – Simulating Death

8. The correct answer is likely (f). The graph is decreasing, and it likely started steeply and got flatter with each iteration.

Section 2.2: Making a Model Using an Exponential Trendline

10. The trendline most likely will not go through each point exactly.

11. The R^2 value is likely near 1; visually, one should see that the trendline matches the data well.

12. Answers will vary depending on the randomness of the rolled M&Ms. The A-value is likely near the initial population. The b-value is likely near 0.41 for Birth scenarios, and likely near -0.69 for Death scenarios.

13. The variable x represents the iteration number. The value of A is likely close to the initial population, as it represents that parameter.

Section 2.2: Making a Model using First Principles

14. The variable x represents the iteration number. The A-value represents the initial population size. The r-value represents the percentage growth rate. In the case of M&Ms, where we expect the population to grow by 50% each turn, $r = 0.5$.

15. The r-value is -0.5.

16. (a) Positive

    (b) Negative

17. (a) Since there is a 1/6-chance of rolling a 1, we have $r = 1/6 \approx 0.1667$. That's about a 16.67% growth rate.

    (b) The first principles model would be
    $y = 30(1 + 0.1667)^x = 30(1.6667)^x$.

18. (a) Since there is a 1/3-chance of rolling a 1 or a 2, we have $r = -1/3 \approx -0.3333$. That's about a 33.33% decay rate (we could also call it a "-33.33% growth rate).

    (b) The first principles model would be $y = 80\big(1 + (-0.3333)\big)^x = 80(0.6667)^x$.

19. Answers will vary depending on where the table is placed. If one places the table such that **Iterations** is in cell A1 and **Model Data** is in cell B1, then =4*(1+0.5)^A2 is an appropriate formula.

21. (a) No (at least, not yet in this text).

    (b) No (at least, not yet in this text).

    (c) Yes (at least, it should).

    (d) If a trendline goes through each point exactly, it matches the data exactly, giving a R^2 value of 1.

22. Excel shows that =exp(0.4055) is 1.500052, which is obviously really close to 1.5. If Excel showed more digits of the 0.4055 number, we'd get a number even closer to 1.5.

23. (a) The initial population is probably close to 15.2; it is likely 15.

    (b) Excel computes =exp(0.1398) as 1.150044. That corresponds to an approximate growth rate of 15%.

24. (a) The initial population is probably close to 231.8.

    (b) Excel computes =exp(-0.2231) as $0.800035 \approx 1 + (-0.2)$. That corresponds to an approximate decay rate of 20%.

25. (a) Increasing

    (b) Decreasing

26. There are several assumptions that can be stated.

    - No color of candy was more likely to land "M"-side up than another.

    - Each M&M has a 50% chance of landing "M"-side up when rolled.

    - When rolling a lot of M&Ms, about half will land "M"-side up.

Section 2.3: Understanding Data Trends with Linear Trendlines

1. 134.5 people per year

2. (a) The trendline seems to have a value of about 4000 at $x = 1766$.

    (b) Using $x = 1766$, the equation of the trendline approximates a population of $134.5 * 1776 - 233449 = 4078$ people.

3. The French and Indian Wars begin in 1754, driving down the population of Augusta County. Our approximations are over-approximations.

4. (a) The trendline has equation $y = 204.23x - 357,718$.

    (b) i. The trendline seems to have a value of about 3000 in the year 1766.

       ii. The equation of the trendline approximates the population as $204.23 * 1776 - 357718 = 2952$ people.

5. The relative error is
$$\left| \frac{2952 - 2873}{2873} \right| = \frac{79}{2873} \approx 0.03 = 3\%.$$
The relative error is about 3%. The approximation is likely good enough to use in research.

6. (a) The trendline for that period of time is $y = 183.22x - 320624$, where x is the year.

    (b) As the slope of the trendline is 183.22, the population grew by about 183 people per year.

7. (a) The trendline of the data is $y = -36,067x + 7E + 07$.

    (b) It does not match the data well. The data climbs steeply, drops significantly from 1989 to 1990, then remains relatively flat after that until about 2013.

8. (a) "=A2 - 1980".

    (b) "=B2/1000000"

    (c)

    (d) i. The years were shifted; the population was scaled.

       ii. To shift, we add/subtract. To scale, we multiply/divide.

    (e) The new trendline has equation $y = -0.0361x + 3.5561$.

    (f) The y-intercept is easier to understand as it no longer has an "E" in it, though the slope is a bit harder to understand.

9. It represents that the number of visitors, in 1980, was about 3.56 million people. This is obviously more than the actual number; it is an approximation.

10. It represents that the number of visitors seems to be dropping by about 0.036 million people per year.

11. No. As stated before, the trendline doesn't really model the data well. There is an uptick in recent years that is not well reflected by the trendline.

12. (a) Using data from 2013-2017 seems reasonable. There isn't a 'right' answer, though. Similar ranges may be chosen.

    (b) Using data from 2013-2017, the trendline is $y = 0.3249x - 8.483$, where x is still the number of years since 1980 and the population is in millions of people. Of course, different year ranges will have different trendline equations.

    (c) Using data from 2013-2017 and the trendline above, we predict 3.8632 million visitors - 3,863,200 visitors.

13. Our approximation was off by about $325,000$ people. While this is not a small number, it corresponds to a relative error of about 9% which is not unreasonably large.

14. September; it is 9 more than 24, 3 less than 36.

15. It should be $(10, 168.031)$.

16. $y = -71.721x + 910.69$, where x is the number of month starting in 2015.

17. Not necessarily. Park/seashore attendance is seasonal, with attendance dropping as the weather turns colder and kids go back to school.

18. The trendline would not be useful for two reasons. First, it predicts negative attendance, so clearly the model fails. Secondly, if we recognize that attendance is seasonal, we don't have enough information to make a good prediction of February attendance.

19. There are many methods one could use. Two of many possible answers are given here.
One could make a simple linear trendline of *just the July attendances*. Recording these numbers in thousands of people with July, 2012 being represented by $x = 1$, the trendline is $y = -7.8371x + 396.17$.
Thus July, 2016 is represented by $x = 5$, and $y(5) = 356.98$, or about 357,000 people.
One could also just model using 2016 data as it is roughly linear. This gives an estimation of about 361,000.

20. Factors like weather, the state of the economy, gas prices, attendance behavior at other parks, and general travel predictions are among the many possible relevant factors.

21. The data is very scattered. It does not appear linear.

22. The data, though scattered, trends upward.

23. The trendline's equation is $y = 3.3948x - 86.66$. This indicates that an increase of 1in in height approximately corresponds to a 3.39lb gain in weight.

24. The height of 5' 8" corresponds to a height of 68". The trendline predicts a weight of about 144lbs. In terms of an educated guess, this is the best approximation we can make and better than a blind guess. At the same time, we don't have any confidence that this number is exactly right. There is clearly a lot of fluctuation in the data.

Section 2.4: Understanding Data Trends with Nonlinear Trendlines

1. Quadratic: $y = 0.3496x^2 - 13.905x + 185.55$;
cubic: $y = 0.0132x^3 - 1.0015x^2 + 30.367x - 278.42$;
quartic:
$y = 0.0003x^4 - 0.0328x^3 + 1.2841x^2 - 18.691x + 104.78$.

2. The quadratic fits well and is simplest. With it, we estimate the weight to be about 364lbs.

3. With the quadratic, the weight is estimated at 102.9lbs, i.e, about 103lbs;
the cubic gives an estimate of 103.8lbs, or 104lbs;
the quartic gives an estimate of 63.4lbs.

4. The model is
$y = 0.0003x^4 - 0.0057x^3 + 0.1305x^2 + 4.1885x + 36.667$.
A deer with chest girth of 32.5" corresponds to $x = 12.5$ in this model, and the weight is estimated to be 105.6lbs.

5. Problem #2 is the extrapolation and #3 is the interpolation. When we interpolate, we are estimating values between known data points; extrapolation is where we approximate beyond our given data range.

6. quadratic: $y = 0.0685x^2 + 5.7354x + 9.9755$
cubic: $y = -0.0482x^3 + 1.5133x^2 - 6.6416x + 37.426$
quartic:
$y = -0.0052x^4 + 0.1606x^3 - 1.3x^2 + 7.8686x + 14.816$
The quartic fits very well, though using our rule of thumb, the quadratic may be the best choice. It fits well and is simple.

7. Regardless of the model chosen, the weight should be about 77lbs.

8. The trendlines for the cubic and quartic drop significantly; the quadratic rises significantly. None of these trendlines seem to make a reasonable prediction.

9. The trendline is $y = 3x + 10$ and it fits the data exactly. The slope of 3 is the constant rate of change of mold spore growth. The y-intercept is the initial population.

10. The equation is $y = 10e^{0.6931x}$; The A-value is 10; it represents the initial population.

11. We have $b = 0.6931$, and $e^b = 1.999906$.

12. The new equation is $y = 5e^{1.0986x}$.

13. The A value is 5.

14. $e^b = 2.99996 \approx (1 + 2)$. Each day the population triples, which means it each day it increases by 200% of what it was the previous day.

15. $y = 1024e^{-0.693x}$

16. $e^b = 0.50002 \approx 0.5 = (1 + (-0.5))$. The growth rate is -1/2; each day, the population decreases by 50% of what it was the previous day.

Section 2.5: Mile Runs

1. A linear trendline seems best for this data, with equation $y = -0.3933x + 1007.1$ and $R^2 = 0.9774$.

4. (a) The years are given where the running record was broken. If one were to interpolate between record–breaking years, one wouldn't find the time of another record.

(b) One can view the trendline as showing a general trend of men's run times decreasing. The trendline for the data has a slope of -0.3933, meaning that the world record time *tends* to drop by about 0.4 seconds per year.

The trendline approximates the world record in 1940 as 244.098 seconds.

(c) The trendline predicts a run time of 212.634 seconds, 11 seconds faster than the current record. This seems unreasonable; it is not likely that the record will be broken by 11 seconds when most other times in history the record is broken by one or two seconds.

Section 2.5: Netflix DVD Subscribers

1. By the curved nature of the data, either a quadratic or exponential model seems appropriate. When forecasting three years forward (as asked below) to the year 2022, the quadratic model predicts DVD subscribers to *increase*. As this is very unlikely, the exponential model seems best.

Using the data as given gives very large numbers in the trendline equation. Shifting the x-values to "years since 2010" gives the exponential model $y = 51.522e^{-0.186x}$ with $R^2 = 0.9988$.

4. (a) The x-value of 2013.5 would correspond to halfway through the 2013 year; it could be used to approximate the number of subscribers in June/July of 2013.

   If the exponential model given above is used, we need to approximate the subscribers with $x = 3.5$. Doing so predicts 26.87 million subscribers.

   (b) The exponential model given above can be used (with $x = 12$) to predict 5.53 million subscribers in 2022. This seems reasonable; while many people are switching to streaming services, many will still see value in the DVD service.

5. The b-value of the exponential model is -0.186. Computing $e^{-0.186} = 0.83 = 1 + (-0.17)$. That is, the number of DVD subscribers is decreasing at a rate of 17% per year.

Section 2.5: Netflix Streaming Subscribers

1. As the data show a slight curve, a linear model does not seem appropriate, pointing rather to a quadratic or exponential model. Either is appropriate.

   If one just highlights the number of subscribers and makes a scatterplot, x represents "quarters since Q2 of 2011", as the first data point corresponds to $x = 1$. One can separately add x-values starting at 0, giving the meaning "quarters since Q3 of 2011." In question #4 you'll be asked to come up with a better system, which you can attempt now.

4. (a) A goal here is to pick x-values that "make sense" or are "easy to work with." These are qualitative

features, meaning there isn't one "right" answer. But with those goals in mind, it should make sense to start numbering at the beginning of a year (i.e., Q1) and not in the middle. Also, letting $x = 1$ correspond to Q1, $x = 2$ correspond to Q2, etc., for some year, also makes sense.

   We need to decide where to start counting. There are two choices that one should consider: starting in 2010 (because starting at a decade seems nice), or starting in 2013, as that's where the data start.

   There are many choices, and these are just suggestions. Picking one that makes the most sense to you will help you understand and explain the situation better.

   (b) Exponential models will have the same b-value. Quadratic models will have the same coefficient on the x^2 term.

5. (a) Starting near the 30th data point, or Q2 2020, seems reasonable.

   (b) Using a linear model on the data from Q2 2022, we approximate 232.85 million subscribers at Q4 2022.

Section 2.5: Netflix Revenue

1. The curved nature of the data indicates a linear trendline would not be appropriate. When modeling with either a quadratic or exponential trendline, the large x-values give equations that are hard to use.

   Shifting the x-values to "years since 2000" gives a quadratic trendline of $y = 133.82x^2 - 1782.1x + 5528.7$ and an exponential model of $y = 162.04e^{0.2542x}$. Each has its strengths and weaknesses.

4. An exponential model forecasts revenue in 2022 at 43,488 million dollars, which is $43.488 billion.

   A quadratic model forcasts the income at 31,091.38 million dollars, which is about $31 billion.

5. The exponential model is $y = 162.04e^{0.2542x}$. One can find that $e^b = e^{0.2542} \approx 1.289$. That corresponds to a 28.9% annual growth rate.

Section 2.5: Smartphones

1. Shifting the x-values to start at 9, representing "years since 2000" gives more manageable numbers in any model's equation.

   Of linear, quadratic, cubic and exponential, the cubic model fits best. It has equation $y = -6.3431x^3 + 234.45x^2 - 2619.3x + 9383.6$. One can make a case that other models are more appropriate.

3. The most likely reason is "market saturation." That is, by 2017 most people who will get a smartphone have one, and those who have a smartphone aren't necessarily replacing theirs every year.

4. Shifting the *x*-values to be "Years since 2000", the linear trendline has equation $y = 225.33x - 1924.6$. The units of the slope are "millions of units per year"; the trendline shows us that between 2009 and 2015, the number of global smartphone shipments was increasing at a near constant rate of 225 million per year.

Section 2.5: Tesla

1. One can make a case for a linear, quadratic or exponential model. (A cubic model fits best, but violates the "use the simplest model that fits well" principle.)

   One should shift the *x*-values to the numbers are not so large. A good choice is to shift the *x*-values by 2010, so that *x* represents "years since 2010."

4. After removing the first data point, the remaining data appear linear. The slope of the linear trendline is 131. This tells us the number of delivered Teslas is increasing at a rate of 131,000 cars per year.

5. The linear model for the data is $y = 131x - 809.95$, where *x* is "years since 2010". With that model, the year 2022 corresponds to $x = 12$. The model predicts 762.05 thousand (i.e., $762,050$) Teslas delivered in 2022.

Section 2.6: Corn Syrup

1. In 1970, the average daily caloric consumption of HFCS was 2 calories per day; in 1980, it was 53 calories per day.

2. In 1970, the average person consumed 730 calories that year from HFCS ($2 \times 365 = 730$). In 1980, the average person consumed 19,345 calories that year from HFCS (53×365; if one recognizes that 1980 is a leap year, then the yearly total is 19,398 calories.)

3. In 1970, the 730 yearly calories from HFCS corresponds to $730/99 = 7.4$ cans of soda per year. In 1980, the 19,345 yearly calories corresponds to $19,345/99 \approx 195$ cans of soda per year.

4. The trendline fits well; $R^2 = 0.9899$.

5. The coefficients are not easy to understand, containing things like "4E-07". Note that these difficult coefficients appear even though we have shifted our data.

6. Approximately 190 calories per day.

7. The first answer is most accurate. The polynomial "predicts" rapid growth in corn syrup consumption, but this is not connected to actual human production and consumption. Polynomials *do not* detect subtle trends in data.

8. Yes, as the lines go through each data point.

9. There is one less trendline than data points. If the data runs from 1970 to 2019, then there are 49 individual trendlines. This isn't manageable on a practical level.

10. Our modeling paradigm suggests that we use only the last two data points when making a prediction, which leads to a prediction of about 85 calories/day.

11. The second statement is most accurate. General trends are not captured by this "connect the dots" approach to modeling.

12. While it fits the data well, outside of the data range (i.e., when extrapolating) they often exhibit extreme/unreasonable growth or decay.

13. There are just too many functions to handle, and general trends are missed.

14. There isn't a definitive "right" answer here. Many note that the HFCS consumption grows steadily until 1999, then declines after that. Therefore a common answer is to make the second interval from 1985 until 1999, and the final interval from 1999 to 2019.

16. A quadratic works best for 1970-1985: $y = 0.5986x^2 - 1.0915x + 2.9011$.

    If one chooses the second interval to be 1985-1999, a linear equation is probably best: $y = 3.7129x + 66.629$. (This equation is based on the years 1985-1999; your equation will be similar, yet different, if you incorrectly only plotted the data from 1986-1999.)

    For 1999-2019, a linear equation is probably best: $y = -4.0645x + 300.62$

17. Visually, one can see the predicted HFCS consumption is a little under 80 calories per day; with the trendline, we find the predicted calories consumed per day is $77 = -4.0645 \times 55 + 300.62$. This is similar to our prediction based on the last two data points, but takes into consideration a longer-term trend.

Chapter 3

Section 3.1: Communicating Data

1. (a) There is more trash.

   (b) We are not told where is the trash located. No units are given for the *y*-axis, so we really don't know how much trash we are talking about. (Is it "bags of trash"? "Tons of trash"? "Barges of trash"?)

   Another serious error that is easy to overlook comes with the use of images/icons to display a value. Consider how the 1990 trash can is almost twice as tall as the 1980 trash can. Because the image is scaled up, the the 1990 trash can is also about twice as *wide*, meaning overall, the *area* of the 1990 trash can is almost 4 times the area of the 1980 trash can! By looking at the graphic, one may subconsciously think the amount of trash has nearly quadrupled, not just doubled.

2. (a) How people want to celebrate an NHS birthday.

   (b) When one adds up all the percentages shown, one gets more than 100%. That *may* be ok, depending on how this data was collected. (For instance, they could ask people "From the list below, choose all that interest you." Since people get more than one choice, the percentages will add up to more than 100. However, in such a case, listing the number of votes vs. percentages would be less confusing.

The cake platter is also a pie chart, but some of the pie slices are hidden by the cake. The color scheme is also hard to discern: lots of shades of purple that are nearly identical, plus (oddly) two shades of gray.

3. (a) It seems to be the result of a poll about viewer fears related to the Zika virus.

   (b) The bar heights do not match the listed percentages.

4. (a) The title seems clear: the graphic is supposed to show why a Big Mac is cheaper than a salad.

   (b) The graphic does not make a direct link between the information given and the title. One has to think hard to understand what the graphic is *probably* trying to convey. (It seems the amount of federal subsidies do not align with federal dietary recommendation, and presumably that means the "wrong" kinds of foods are cheap.)

5. (a) The most clear result is that *something* changed related to the number of murders after the 2005 Florida 'Stand Your Ground' law.

   (b) The y-axis is upside down, so one can easily conclude the number of gun deaths is going down after 2005 when the number, in fact, increased.

   The red shading is obviously representative of blood, which is gruesome.

6. (a) The chart is showing the annual sales (for an unspecified time period, though probably a year) of various fast-food restaraunt chains. The graph compares these numbers to the GDP of Afghanistan.

   (b) Using icons/images to represent the values is problematic, just as it was in the "Trash" graphic. McDonald's has about 4 times as much sales as Burger King, yet it seems that at least 8 Burger King icons would fit into the McDonald's logo, making McDonald's sales seem at least 8 times bigger.

   The y-axis should be labeled near the y-axis, not with a label in the middle of the graphic.

   Sales of a company are not directly comparable to the Gross Domestic Product (GDP) of a country. It seems that somehow McDonalds is "bigger" than Afghanistan, but it isn't clear exactly "how".

7. (a) The graphic shows how workers in different major U.S. cities commute to work.

   (b) This graphic works fairly well to give a general impression about differences between cities. It clearly lacks specificity, though it probably wasn't trying to convey specific percentages.

Each letter has area concentrated in different ways. For instance, the blue portion of the "L" of "LA" is far larger than the dark red region right above it. However, what matters most is the thickness of the blue vs. dark red regions. One could argue that these differently sized areas could mislead the reader, though it's the opinion of the authors that in this case, that is not really a problem.

8. (a) It is difficult to know the point of this graphic. The title assumes the reader knows what "sufficiency" means in this context.

   (b) Good graphics can "standalone," meaning one can look at the graphic and understand its message without additional, explanatory text. This graphic fails that measure. (For instance, can a happy person be "sufficient" in more than one domain?)

9. (a) The relationship between the balance on a home loan and the equity (i.e., the home value minus the loan amount) in the home.

   (b) The colored circle looks like it could be a stylized pie chart, giving a visual idea of the relationship. However, the orange portion should be smaller than the green portion.

10. (a) Where food consumed in the UK comes from.

    (b) It is immediately clear that the U.K. gets half of its food from the U.K., and the other half comes from a large number of other nations from around the world. A *lot* of other nations are listed, including those that seemingly contribute little. One can't easily recognize the slice size of the smaller countries (say, Columbia). All the listed countries provides a lot of cluttter. A table may be a better way of displaying this type of information.

11. (a) The title is very clear: more students are getting a diploma in 2014 than in previous years.

    (b) The vertical stacking of books is a fine, creative way to represent a bar graph. (I.e., this graph does not suffer from the same mistake as the graphs that use Trash and Fast Food icons.)

    The main shortcoming of this graphic is that the heights of the book stacks implies that number of diplomas has more than doubled from 2008 to 2014. The increase from 75% to 82% may indeed be significant (and corresponding to millions of students), but the graph makes the difference look more dramatic than it is.

12. (a) R.A. Dickey's knuckleball velocity dropped between 2012 and 2013.

    (b) The speed has dropped by 2mph (less than 3%), but the graph makes it look like the speed is half of what it once was.

13. (a) Both the unemployment rate and uninsured rate are growing. Also, by pairing the data, there is an implication that the two growth patterns are related.

(b) In many respects, this graphic is very well constructed. It is acceptable to use two different y-axis scales when showing a relationship between two different types of data (the left axis units are "number of people", and the right axis units are "percent"). The title is clear, the axes are labeled, and different colors are used for the different data sets.

The main drawback is that the number of Uninsured Americans grew by about 3 million people, though the graph makes it look like the number doubled. A similar problem exists for the Unemployment Rate.

Further, graphs like these imply "the graph shows a clear correlation between the data." However, the scales for each y-axis were probably chosen carefully to make the graph have greater impact. If either/both y scales included 0, the growth would look less dramatic and have less similarity.

Section 3.2: Visualizing Data

1. No.

2. Using the average height is probably the most direct way of answering with a single number.

3. Lots of information is lost! When 1500 numbers are reduced to 1 number, about 1499 pieces of information are lost.

4. Not particularly. We know there are some short cadets, some very tall cadets, and lots of cadets who are somewhere in between.

5. Break the data into more than 3 categories.

6. 14 (1+1+5+7)

7. 7 (4+2+1)

8. 443 (169 + 164 + 110)

9. There are too many bins; there are too many individual numbers to consider. Choosing more than 3 bins, but less than 23 given here would be good. Perhaps using a bin size of 2" would be good.

10. 44

11. 82 (75 + 7)

12. The larger the data set, the more bins that are needed, though if too many bins are used, it can be hard to understand. General rules of thumb suggest between 5 and 20 bins, depending on the number of data points and the range of values within the data.

13. d; a & b are not good options because by a similar logic, VT students are also *shorter* than VMI students. Option c isn't good either as the table wasn't misread. The phrase "tend to be taller" isn't clearly defined, but most would consider more information than just number in the tallest class.

14. Change the tables to show *relative frequency* instead of *counts*, or frequency.

15.

Height (inches)	% of VT Students	Height (inches)	% of VMI Cadets
less than 55	0.01	less than 55	0.00
55 to 59	0.81	55 to 59	0.46
60 to 64	18.64	60 to 64	7.69
65 to 69	41.99	65 to 69	40.01
70 to 74	33.71	70 to 74	46.45
75 to 79	4.79	75 to 79	5.32
more than 79	0.04	more than 79	0.07

16. About 4.83% of VT students are 75" or taller; about 5.39% of VMI students are 75" or taller.

17. No; a higher percentage of VMI students are "tall" than VT students.

18. About 8.15% of VMI students are shorter than 65". Thus out of 70 students, we would expect $70 \times 8.15\% = 5.7$, or 6, students to be shorter than 65".

19. VT has a higher percentage of women than VMI, and hence has a higher percentage of people who are in the 60-64" range than VMI; as VMI has a higher percentage of men than VT, VMI has a higher percentage of people in the 70-74" range.

21. Populations A & B. Population D *almost* is bell-shaped, but is just a little too non-symmetric.

23. The term "spread" hasn't been defined yet, but we'll take it to mean the distance between the lowest and highest numbers on the histogram.

   (a) Population B has the most spread: 81 - 60 = 21.

   (b) Population C has the least spread: 75 - 71 = 4.

24. (a) 66%: (0.04 + 0.2 + 0.42 = 0.66)

   (b) 33%: (0.26 + 0.06 + 0.01 = 0.33)

25. Alpha Company (the tallest cadets): Population C

   Delta Company (shorter than Alpha Co., with less spread/variation than male or female cadets): Population D

   Female Cadets (bell shaped): Population A

   Male Cadets (bell shaped, higher numbers than female cadets): Population B

26. Right

27. 10 or more (3.68% + 0.61% + 0.61% = 4.9%

28. This is hard to answer as we haven't yet defined "center". About half of the cadets did less than 1 pull up, so doing 1 pull-up puts one "in the middle". So we'll say that the center is about 1 pull-up.

29. We would expect roughly the same number of cadets to be born each month, so tht distribution is expected to be uniform. The other two data sets (cadet weights and SAT scores) probably look bell-shaped, or normal: lots of people in the middle, with fewer cadets in the extreme highs & lows.

33. What stands out depends on the reader.

    It appears that some have completed the 1.5 mile run in less than 2 minutes; that is suspicious.

34. About 76%; about 30% + 32% + 14%.

35. About 480 seconds (8 minutes). One can see that the 420-479 bin has about 2 or 3% in it; therefore, if one's time is in that bin, then one is faster than the rest of the Corps (the other 98 or 97%).

Section 3.3: Measures of Center

1. (a) The mean of data set A is 0; the mean of data set B is 20.

    (b) No, the mean isn't necessarily a value in the data set.

    (c) The mean of data set A seems to be an intuitive measure of center.

    (d) The mean of data set B seems to be a poor measure of the center.

    (e) Most of the data in B are zeros, with one entry being 100. This 100 makes the middle seem larger than our intuition expects.

2. Data set A, sorted, is 1,3,5,7,8. The median is the middle value of 5.

    Data set B, sorted, is 1,5,7,8. The median is the mean of the two middle numbers 5 and 7, so the median is 6.

3. (a) No.

    (b) It depends on how many students *are* 68" tall.

    (c) At most 12 students are shorter than 68" tall, and at most 12 students are taller than 68" tall.

    (d) The answer does not change. Since 25 is an odd number, we know there is one student who is exactly 68" tall (the "middle" student). The 12 "shorter" students could all be 68" tall, or they could each be less than 68" tall. So we can say there are at most 12 students shorter than 68" tall

4. The mean is 69.4", and the median is 70".

5. For data set A, the mean and median are both 0.
    For data set B, the mean is 2 and the median is 0.

    (a) The median is better.

    (b) No.

6. (a) Data set A: mean is 19.6; median is 0.
        Data set B: mean is 20; median is 0.

    (b) The mean changed more when the largest value got bigger.

7. (a) In A, the outlier is −200.
        In B, the outlier is 200.
        In C, the outliers are both −200 and 200.

    (b) A: mean is −39.6, median is 0.
        B: the mean is 39.6, median is 0.
        C: mean and median are 0.

    (c) Outliers have a bigger impact on the mean.

    (d) In C, the outliers "cancel each other out."

8. (a) Increase

    (b) Remain unchanged

9. (a) Decrease

    (b) Remain unchanged

10. The median is unaffected by outliers.

11. (a) The first one is normal; the second is not normal, skew nor uniform.

    (b) Skew right.

12. 23% of women had 0 pull ups, an additional 29% had 1. Since 23% + 29% is bigger than 50%, the middle value must be 1.

14. 65%

15. median

16. height

17. The mean is a fine predictor with a normal distribution. It is not a good predictor with a skewed distribution.

18. Yes.

19. (a) decrease

    (b) increase

Section 3.4: Measures of Variation

1. (a) The two shapes are very different. On the left is a uniform distribution; on the right is a symmetric.

    (b) They appear to be within about 2" of each other - about the same.

    (c) The histogram on the right, which includes all cadet heights.

2. A shows more variation. Because it is a uniform distribution, many mistakenly think this corresponds to less variation. However, it means that there are about as many people very far from the mean as there are near the mean: there is a lot of variation.

3. D, though it isn't necessarily obvious why. One clue is that the overall range of data in D is larger.

4. (a) The whole corps of cadets will have the most variation (it is the most diverse population).

    (b) The group of female cadets seems to have the least amount of variation.

5. Female: mean = 64.5", std. dev = 2.9"
    male: mean = 70.0", std. dev = 3.0"
    corps: mean = 69.4", std. dev = 3.4"

6. Yes, it should.

7. Inches

8. This is a prediction based on the spread and shape of the data. Read on to find out which is actually larger.

9. (All units are pull ups.)
    female: mean = 2.6, std. dev. = 3.0
    male: mean = 10.5, std. dev. = 5.7
    corps: mean 9.7, std. dev = 6.0

10. height: mean = 69.4", std. dev. = 3.4"
    pull ups: mean = 9.7 pull ups, std. dev = 6.0 pull ups.

11. One may be tempted to say "There is more variation in the pull up data than in the height data." While one number is larger, since they have different units, they really are not comparable. It is similar to asking "Who has more fruit: Alice, who has 5 apples, or Gary, who has 10 grapes?" One number is larger, yet the units (i.e., type of fruit) makes a big difference.

12. The standard deviation can be 0. A data set where every value is the same has no variation – the standard deviation is 0.
    The standard deviation cannot be negative.

13. 33 pullups (33 − 0).

14. 23" (80 − 57)

15. Advantages include it is intuitive to understand and easy to compute. Disadvantages include that for large data sets, it may be hard to find the largest/smallest values (by hand), and it is greatly affected by outliers.

16. The range

17. Pullups:
    Min = 0, Q1 = 5, median = 9, Q3 = 14, Max = 33, IQR = 9
    Heights:
    Min = 57, Q1 = 67, Median = 70, Q3 = 72, Max = 80, IQR = 5

18. In comparison, the distribution for (a) will be shorter & wider, while the distribution for (b) will be taller & skinny.

19. It is a measure of how far apart the middle 50% of the data is.

20. a., greater variation

21.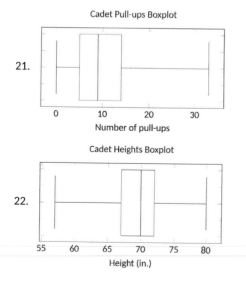

Cadet Pull-ups Boxplot

22.

Cadet Heights Boxplot

Cadet Height Box and Whisker Plot

23.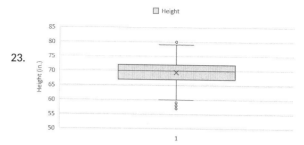

Section 3.5: Measures of Relative Standing

1. No; you would need to know all the other data values in the population, though a measure of variation/spread would be useful, too.

2. The histogram should be "tall and narrow", with most bars below the 120 value.

3. The histogram should be "short and wide", with the histogram containing many bars beyond 120.

4. In the second sketch - the variation/spread is greater.

5. (a) increases
    (b) increases
    (c) less
    (d) decreases

Statistics	Red	Population Blue	Green
Mean	99.18	99.56	98.78
Standard Deviation	4.93	10.37	19.88
Q1	96.00	93.00	86.00
Median	99.00	100.00	99.00
Q3	102.00	107.00	112.25
Q3 - Q1	6.00	14.00	26.25
5th Percentile	91.00	82.95	65.00
95th Percentile	107.00	117.00	129.00
Percentile of IQ = 120	NA	0.97	0.85

6.

7. The max value of the Red group is less than 120.

8. a, decreases

9. b, increases

10. a, decreases

11. Green

12. Green

13. Red

14. b, the standard deviation decreases

		Red	Population Blue	Green
X - 2s	IQ Value	89.32	78.82	59.02
	Percentile	0.023	0.019	0.023
X - 1s	IQ Value	94.25	89.19	78.90
	Percentile	0.169	0.169	0.154
X + 1s	IQ Value	104.11	109.93	118.66
	Percentile	0.857	0.841	0.834
X + 2s	IQ Value	109.04	120.30	138.54
	Percentile	0.980	0.971	0.982

15.

16. 2.5th percentile

17. 97.5th percentile

18. About 95%

19. Unusually high is above $\bar{x} + 2s$, or larger than two standard deviations above the mean. Unusually low would be less than $\bar{x} - 2s$.

20. (a) $z = \dfrac{126 - 99.56}{10.37} = 2.84$

    (b) $z = \dfrac{93 - 99.56}{10.37} = -0.63$

21. No; they are different stats from different sports, with expected values in different ranges.

22. The vertical line will be at $6.59 + 2(4.94) = 16.47$ PPG. About 97% of all players are below this mark.

23. The line will be at 22.9 PPG.

24. It looks as though at least 99% of NBA playwers have a PPG game below Bryant's, nearly 100%. The percentage above Bryant is very small, less than 1%.

25. Kobe Bryant's average PPG was greater than almost all other NBA players, making him one of the greatest NBA players.

26. The line will be drawn at $0.273 + 2(0.026) = 0.325$. About 98% of all MLB players have a batting average less than this, including Jeter.

27. The vertical line will be at 0.310.

28. Using the percentages on the histogram, we approximate that Jeter's BA is higher than 96% of all MLB players.

29. Derek Jeter's batting average was better than 96% of all MLB players, making him one of the greatest hitters of all time.

30. Bryant's percentile is at least 99%, very close to 100%. His z-score is $(22.9 - 6.59)/4.94 = 3.30$.

    Jeter's percentile is about 96%, and his z-score is $(0.310 - 0.273)/0.026 = 1.42$.

    While there is more to baseball than BA, and more to basketball than PPG, Bryant is the clear winner of this contest. He is in a higher percentile, and has a higher z-score.

Chapter 4

Section 4.1: Probability

1.

	Dec.	Incon.	Truth	Total
Guilty	41	3	6	50
Inn.	27	5	18	50
Total	68	8	24	100

2. 68 participants

3. $\frac{41}{50}$

4. 82%

5. 0.82

6. $\frac{41}{68}$

7. 60.3%

8. 0.603%

9. A police detective won't know innocence/guilt in advance, so the probability in Question 5 isn't of much use. Rather, he/she will give the test to someone in hope of determining their guilt.

10. $\frac{59}{100}$

11. $\frac{33}{100}$

12. We expect $0.59 \times 300 = 177$ people to receive a correct result.

13. $P(\text{Guilty and Deceptive}) = \frac{41}{100}$

14. $P(\text{Innocent and Deceptive}) = \frac{27}{100}$

15. $P(\text{Deceptive}) = \frac{68}{100}$

16. $P(\text{Deceptive}) = \frac{68}{100}$, it matches

17. $P(\text{Guilty person was Deceptive}) = \frac{41}{50}$

18. $P(\text{Innocent person was Deceptive}) = \frac{27}{50}$

19. $\frac{68}{50}$, this is not possible. The probability is over 1; it does not make sense to add these probabilities together.

20. (a) They are already known to be guilty.

    (b) 41 participants.

    (c) 50 participants.

    (d) $P(\text{Deceptive} \mid \text{Guilty}) =$ the number of both Deceptive and Guilty divided by the number of Guilty.

    (e) There are 18 participants who are Truthful and Innocent, and there are 50 Innocent participants. Therefore $P(\text{Truthful} \mid \text{Innocent}) = \frac{18}{50}$.

21. $P(\text{Guilty} \mid \text{Deceptive}) = \frac{41}{68}$. Yes, it is conditional having a Deceptive Result.

22. Answers will vary; in brief, look at the number in the Guilty row and Inconclusive column, then divide that number by the total of the Guilty row.

23. $P(\sim\text{Deceptive}) = \frac{32}{100}$.

24. (a) Answers will vary; in general, one would want to see a significantly lower percentage of the vaccinated population getting sick than the unvaccinated population.

    (b) Answers will vary; certainly, far fewer vaccinated people contracted Covid than those who got the placebo.

    (c) Answers will vary; one could assign a percent based on how many cases of infection were stopped.

25. $196/28207 = 0.00694$

26. (a) $11/196 = 0.056$

    (b) $P(V \mid C)$

27. (a) $11/14134 = 0.00078$

      (b) $P(C|V)$

28.   (a) 185/14073 = 0.0131%

      (b) $P(C|{\sim}V)$

29.   (a) From Question 28, we have the proportion 185/14073; that is, without vaccination, we expect about 1.31% of the population to contract Covid.

         From Question 27, we get the proportion 11/14134; that is, we expect about 0.078% of the vaccinated population to get Covid.

         Divide these two percentages: 0.078%/1.31% = 5.9%. That is, only 5.9% of those who we would "expect" to get Covid actually got sick; in other words, the vaccine prevented about 94.1% of infections.

      (b) The calculation in (a) explains the meaning of the number; this is a reasonable way of determining efficacy.

30. 159/1356 = 0.117

31. 285/1312 = 0.217

32. P(Capstone|Good)

33. 22/875 = 0.025

34. P(Defective|Apex)

35.   (a) P(Apex|Defective)

      (b) Apex makes the most boots, so it isn't surprising they have the most defective boots.

      (c) P(Defective|Apex) = 0.025;
         P(Defective|Baseline) = 0.044;
         P(Defective|Capstone) = 0.05;

36. 0.05 * 40 = 2.

Section 4.2: Sampling

1. 10 boxes

28.   (a) 10%

      (b) Most students will have 0; some may have 1 or 2.

      (c) Most answers will fall between a 10% and 20% difference.

      (d) The MAX command.

      (e) Answers will vary, expect between 60 and 80.

      (f) Answers will vary, though they should be within 5% about 50% of the time. In this simulation, about 40 to 60 times out of 100.

29.   (a) 10%

      (b) Probably never.

      (c) Most answers will fall between a 8% and 13% difference.

      (d) Most answers will be in the high 70s to low 80s.

      (e) Answers will vary, though they should be within high 60s to low 70s.

30.   (a) 100 × 10,000 = 1,000,000

      (b) Answers will vary. Ultimately, not very long when one considers the number of things being calculated.

31.   (a) 1%

      (b) Probably never.

      (c) Most answers will fall between a 8% and 13% difference.

      (d) Most answers will be in the high 70s to low 80s.

      (e) Answers will vary, though they should be within high 60s to low 70s.

Section 4.3: Confidence Intervals for Proportions

1. a & b

2. To increase the confidence level, we need to increase the confidence interval size, or widen the interval.

4. Increase

5.   (a) Increase

      (b) ii, increase the sample size n.

6. The size N of the population is missing.

7.   (a) The margin of error is $E = 0.052$.

      (b) The confidence interval is $0.55 \pm 0.052 = (0.498, 0.602)$.

      (c) We have 70% confidence that the population proportion of Adams supporters is between 49.8% and 60.2%.

8.   (a) The margin of error is $E = 0.098$, so the interval is $(0.452, 0.648) \approx (0.45, 0.65)$.

      (b) The E value is larger than in question #7 (a).

      (c) The confidence interval is larger than in problem 7 (b).

9.   (a) The margin of error is $E = 0.031$, so the confidence interval is $(0.519, 0.581)$.

      (b) The margin of error is smaller than in problem 8.

      (c) The confidence interval is smaller than in problem 8.

10. In this situation, $E = 0.183$, meaning our sampled proportion may be about 18 percentage points away from the true proportion. Saying "Adams enjoys between 37% and 73% of the popular vote" does not seem to convey much useful information.

11.   (a) The margin of error is $E = 0.039$. Thus the interval is $(0.601, 0.679)$.

(b) Several things may be discussed here. The most egregious error is that it quite common for people today to not have a landline phone, hence not have a number listed in the phone book, where the population without a land line tends to be much younger than those with. Also, there are a significant number of people with landlines with unlisted numbers. Therefore randomly selecting from the phone book likely is not a good way of sampling all Roanoke residents.

12. $n = \hat{p}(1 - \hat{p})\dfrac{z^2}{E^2}$.

13. Using $E = 0.01$ and $z = 2.575$, we get $n = 16577$.

14. (a) Using $E = 0.03$ and $z = 2.575$, we get $n = 1842$.

    (b) The first n value was 9 times as large as the second.

15. Using $E = 0.03$, $z = 2.575$, $\hat{p} = 0.01$ and $(1 - \hat{p}) = 0.99$, we get $n = 73$.

Section 4.4: Confidence Intervals for Means

1. There isn't a right or wrong answer, though most are not surprised to find the mean is actually 45 or 51, and most are surprised to find it is 30.

2. There isn't a right or wrong answer, though with the increased sample size, we are more confident in our approximation. Most are not surprised to find the mean is actually 51, and are likely surprised if it is 45, 60 or 30.

3. We are likely more confident in Population #2, as there is less variation in that dataset.

4. $t = 2.093024$

5. (a)

   (b) $t = 2.022$

   (c) $t = 2.708$

   (d) $t = 1.984$

   (e) $t = 1.962$

6. (a) t gets larger as the confidence level increases, causing the interval size to also increase. Again, we are casting a "wider net" to gain confidence we "catch" the true mean.

   (b) t gets smaller as n increases, decreasing the size of the confidence interval. Sampling a larger number increases accuracy.

7. 0.02 corresponds to the 80% confidence level; with $n = 50$ there are 49 degrees of freedom.

8. It multiplies the t-value with the standard deviation, divided by the square root of the sample size.

9. The `if` statement returns `Yes` if the value in B8 is less than E and `No` if it is not.

11. Cadets most likely will see anywhere from 1-9 No's; however, most refreshes should yield answer close to 4 No's (indicating that the population mean is falling within the confidence interval around 80% of the time).

12. (a) (6.62, 7.06) pounds

    (b) (5.75, 6.15) pounds

    (c) Yes. The entire confidence interval for the babies with prenatal cocaine exposure is below the control group's confidence interval.

13. (a) (33, 34) cm

    (b) (31.8, 32.6) cm

    (c) Yes. The entire confidence interval for the babies with prenatal cocaine exposure is below the control group's confidence interval.

14. (a) For Diet A, the 95% confidence interval for the mean is $(9.17, 10.83)$ whereas for Diet B it is $(10.95, 13.05)$.

    (b) Based on the 95% confidence interval, it is a true statement as that is a result of the study.

    (c) For Diet A, the 99% confidence interval for the mean is $(8.88, 11.12)$ whereas for Diet B it is $(10.59, 13.41)$.

    (d) Probably. The true mean weight loss for each diet plan likely falls in confidence intervals that do not overlap, but they almost do. For Diet A, the 95% confidence interval for the mean is $(9.17, 10.83)$ whereas for Diet B it is $(10.95, 13.05)$. The 99% confidence intervals *do* overlap.

Section 4.5: An Introduction to Hypothesis Testing

1. No - getting two heads in a row is not an unlikely event.

2. Flip the coin many more times; collect more data.

3. 85/100

4. Yes.

5. No.

6. Yes.

7. Since the stakes are so low, you probably don't care; win or lose, your net worth hasn't really changed. (And that's the point.)

8. With $1000 at stake, you would certainly care about the results of the bet. With a chance of winning at over 98%, many would take the bet.

9. With $1000 at stake, you would likely want to be confident in the result. Many would say that an 11% chance of being wrong is too high a risk.

10. a, reject the null as the *P*-value is less than the significance level.

11. b, fail to reject the null, as the *P*-value is greater than the significance level.

12. a

13. a

14. b

15. b

16. a

17. a

18. a

19. a

Section 4.6: Designing Hypothesis Tests

1. (a) is the null hypothesis, and (b) is the alternate hypothesis.

2. All the null hypotheses have an equal sign in them: either $=$, $\leq$ or $\geq$.

3. a, d, e, f, g

    (b) requires some measure of dolphin/whale/animal intelligence. Supposing we had one, we could write "Is the average dolphin score on the Animal Intelligence Test higher than the average whale score?"

    (c) "Is the yearly average number of colds experienced by those who take Vitamin C lower than the yearly average number of colds experienced by those who do not take Vitamin C?"

    (h) The term 'more popular' is not precisely defined. One measure could be "number of people watching each game." Using that, we could write "Is the average number of viewers of basketball games higher than the average number of viewers of baseball games?"

4. c

5. The null hypothesis is that nothing special happens and includes an equal sign:

    $\mu_1 \leq \mu_2$

6. The alternate hypothesis is that something special is happening:

    $\mu_1 > \mu_2$.

7. a

8. There is enough evidence to show that those who exercise lose more weight, on average, than those who diet.

Section 4.7: Hypothesis Tests Involving Proportions and Means

1. Proportion: percent, proportion, most, likely;
    Mean: average

2. In order, we have: proportion, mean, proportion, mean, proportion, mean

3. If only one group is mentioned, and it's statistic is compared to specific number, then we have a 1-sample test.

    When two groups are mentioned, without a specific number being relevant, we have a 2-sample test.

4. In order, 1-, 2-, 1-, 2- (this is subtle, but we'll compare two different sets of times), 2-, 2-

5. In order, Hyp. Test – 1 Mean, Hyp. Test – 1 Proportion, Hyp. Test – 2 Proportions

6. c

7. $H_0 : \mu \leq 200$, $H_1 > 200$.

8. 201

9. 2

10. 841

11. 200

12. The middle one, corresponding to $\mu > \mu_0$, which is our alternate hypothesis.

13. We reject the null hypothesis as $p = 0$ (i.e., lower than the sign. level).

    "There is sufficient evidence to conclude the average American has a cholesterol level above 200mg/dL."

14. c

15. $H_0 : p \leq 0.5$; $H_1 : p > 0.5$

16. 0.5

17. 1000; the "nearly 5000" surveyed don't count as the sample size as they slept more than 6.8 hours a night.

18. c, $=525/1000$

19. The $p > p_0$ row, as that matches our alternate hypothesis.

20. $P = 0.057$

21. We fail to reject the null hypothesis; "There is insufficient evidence to conclude that the proportion of Americans who sleep less than 6.8 hours a day that have been diagnosed with depression greater than 0.50."

22. a

23. $H_0 : p_1 \geq p_2$; $H_1 : p_1 < p_2$

24. b, $=231/627$

25. The first, $P = 0.094$, as it aligns with our alternate hypothesis.

26. Reject the null hypothesis. "There is sufficient evidence to conclude that those who include organic food in their diet are less likely to have 2 or more colds in a year than those who do not include organic foods."

Section 4.8: Hypothesis Testing for Dependence

1. $68/92 = 0.739$

2. $47/92 = 0.511$

3.

Exp. Counts	Deceptive	Truthful	Total
Guilty	34.74	12.26	47
Innocent	33.26	11.74	45
Total	68	24	92

4. Use '$E3*C5/E5$'.

5. $P = 0.0029$

6. As *P* is less than the significance level, yes, reject the null hypothesis.

7. No, the row and column variables are dependent.

8. Yes; these tests should be dependent on guilt.

9. Yes, they are dependent of each other. This should make common sense; people who attend rallies are probably more likely to vote than those who do not.

Section 4.9: Hypothesis Testing Review

1. (a) iv, 2-sample mean

   (b) v (it may seem that (ii) is the same thing, but it states that "Virginians *don't* spend more time outside", whereas (v) states "we couldn't show Virginians do." It is a subtle, and significant, differe

2. (a) v, Test for Dependence

   (b) iv, rejecting the null means rejecting independence.

3. (a) i, 1-sample proportion

   (b) i

4. (a) v, Test for Dependence

   (b) H_0: gender is independent of preference in quitting-smoking treatment.

   H_1: gender is dependent of preference in quitting-smoking treatment.

   (c) 0.052

(d) Fail to reject. (It is oh-so-close, though! One might need to rethink their threshold.)

(e) There is insufficient evidence to conclude that men and women have differing preferences for treatment to help quit smoking.

5. (a) iii, 1-sample mean

   (b) H_0: $\mu \leq 0$;

   H_1: $\mu > 0$

   (c) $P = 0.02$

   (d) reject the null hypothesis

   (e) There is sufficient evidence to conclude that the weight loss program is effective.

6. (a) i

   (b) H_0: $p \leq .1$;

   H_1: $p > 0.1$

   (c) $P = 0.089$

   (d) Fail to reject the null

   (e) There is insufficient evidence to conclude that 10% or more of the shipment is defective.

   (f) At the 10% confidence level, we would conclude 'reject the null.'

   (g) "There is sufficient evidence to conclude that at least 10% of the shipment is defective."

   (h) Answers will vary. If your goal is quality assurance, you probably would not need much evidence to conclude the batch is defective.

Appendix F

Answers to the Exercises

Section 1.3: Exercises

1. See https://bit.ly/2PSYm7u for help.

3. See https://bit.ly/2PSYm7u for help.

5.
   - Excel usually auto-formats text it recognizes as a date. March 14, 2015 is usually converted to display "14-Mar-15".
   - Subsequent dates are filled into the cells.
   - If the date is placed in cell A1, the formula =TEXT(A1,''dddd'') gives the day of the week. See also https://bit.ly/33e7qXw.

7. The percentage of total food costs decrease. Airfare increased, meaning it takes a larger percentage of overall costs, meaning all other categories decrease.

9. ¥21,791.25

11. It remains at about 18%

13. See CT_Kitchen_SOLUTION for a possible solution.

Section 2.1: Exercises

1. (d), -30

3. (c), $y = 17x + 1500$

5. (d), $y = 16x + 215$

7.
   (a) $146,241 + 4000 = 150,241$ people.
   (b) $146,241 + 8000 = 154,241$ people.
   (c) $146,241 + 10 * 4000 = 186,241$ people.
   (d) $K = 4000n + 146,241$ people. After 15 years, we expect the population to be $4000 * 15 + 146,241 = 206,241$ people.

9.
   (a) Since the coefficient of x is positive, this is a simulation of immigration.
   (b) The slope is 4.8. It should be interpreted as a growth of approximately 5 M&Ms per Iteration.
   (c) The y-intercept is 12 M&Ms and represents the starting number of M&Ms.

   (d) The closest integer to 4.8 is 5, so it is likely that 10 (i.e, 2*5) M&Ms were rolled each turn, starting with 12 M&Ms.

11.
   (a) millions of dollars per year
   (b) $37.3 million dollars

13.
   (a) Letting x be hours since 6:00 a.m. and y be degreesint Fahrenheit, we can use $y = 2x + 45$.
   (b) Noon is 6 hours after 6:00 a.m., so we use $2 * 6 + 45 = 57°$F.
   (c) No; the temperature in the evening is likely decreasing instead of increasing.

15.
   (a) The x-axis should be labeled "Years since 2010"; the y-axis should be labeled "Number of new homes (thousands)"; the title should be similar to "Number of New Homes Sold in the U.S. since 2010."
   (b) The equation is $y = 43.042x + 290.11$ with $R^2 = 0.977$.
   (c) The units are "thousands of homes per year." Each year, we expect 43 thousand more homes to be built than in the previous year.
   (d) With 2022 corresponding to $x = 12$, we approximate $43.042 * 12 + 290.11 = 806.6$ thousand new homes built in 2022.

17. See MM_LinearImmigration_SOLUTION for a possible solution.

Section 2.2: Exercises

1. (c), 20000

3. When $x = 6$, the population is $5,243$ and when $x = 7$, the population is $4,194$. So the population reaches $5,000$ sometime during the 7th week.

5. (b), 700

7. (a), $y = 120(0.75)^x$. Since the population decreases by 1/4, or 25%, each year, the growth rate is $1 + (-0.25) = 0.75$.

9. (b), about 190 people. One can arrive at this answer by computing $110 \times (1.2)^3$, or through approximation and the process of elimination. The population is growing by 20% each year. Since the initial population is a little over 100, in the first year the population will grow by a little more than 20. Repeating this two more times brings us to an approximation somewhere under 200, yet more than 130.

11. See MM_ExpDeath_SOLUTION for a possible solution.

13. (b), an exponential model, as the population is decreasing at constant percent rate.

Section 2.3: Exercises

1. Empirical model

3. Extrapolation; you are approximating a value beyond the range of your collected data.

5. (a): the model was close, and likely gave a better answer than just guessing.

7. (a) It would be useful to shift the Years. There are two good answers. First, one could subtract 2000 from the years, and relabel the x-values as "Years since 2000." Then the x-value of "8" is easily understood to represent "2008."

   One could also shift by 2003, the first data point, and relabel x-values as "Years since 2003." This isn't as intuitive, as the x-value of "8" represents "2011."

   (b) The number of graduates doesn't need to be shifted or scaled. Shifting would cause great confusion. The y-values are not so big that scaling would be useful, either.

9. (a)

11. See DT_LinearTL1_SOLUTION for a possible solution.

Section 2.4: Exercises

1. (b), $y = 3x + 0$

3. (a), Linear trendline

5. (b), Quadratic trendline

7. (a), close to 0. The data does not appear to show any trend or pattern, so a linear model would not fit well.

9. The A value of 0.3217 is not helpful; it tells us the approximate population in "year 0".

   The b value of 0.0103 corresponds to $e^0.0103 = 1.01$, meaning the U.S. has seen a growth rate of about 1% over the past 60 years.

11. See DT_NonLinearTL_SOLUTION1 and DT_NonLinearTL_SOLUTION2 for possible solutions.

Section 2.6: Exercises

1. (b), as the last x-value of the first trendline is to be the first x-value of the second trendline.

3. The bound is around 2010

5. (d), $x = 21$

7. Scale the y-axis by dividing each value by 1,000.

9. See CS_MultiTL_SOLUTION for a possible solution.

Section 3.1: Exercises

1. (b), the general online shopping habits of people in the Nordic region.

3. (c), the number of Americans on welfare greatly increased between 2009-2011.

5. (a); the choice of this answer is strengthened by the fact the graphic was created by Republican staffers (see the fine print at the bottom of the graphic).

7. (a), at a glance, it appears like the approval percentage represents the American people as a whole rather than just Republicans (because "among Republicans" is in small font).

   It isn't clear that there is supposed to be a "Disapproval" bar for the graph; maybe the "Approval" word & percentage is just highlighted.

9. A bar graph. A pie graph is appropriate when the numbers are parts of a whole; a line graph is appropriate when there is a continuum between the data (whereas this data is discrete; there is no value "halfway between" Bill Clinton and George W. Bush).

Section 3.2: Exercises

1. (b), around 67-71 inches.

3. (c), 31.94%

5. 70 inches

7. (c), the data is roughly symmetric.

9. (c), using 5-9 bins best summarizes the data, because you can easily see the shape of the data without having too many classes.

11.

	Uniform Size	Height Range	Number of Uniforms
Female	Small	63" or shorter	101
	Medium	64" to 67"	120
	Large	68" and taller	36
Male	Small	64" or shorter	46
	Medium	65" to 72"	1125
	Large	73 to 76"	278
	X-Large	77" and taller	15

13. See VS_Histogram2_SOLUTION for a possible solution.

Section 3.3: Exercises

1. False

3. c and e.

5. Only 1.

7. c

9. a

11. (a) Mean: $172,250; Median: $164,500.

    (b) The McCorkle Dr. house is an outlier, pulling the mean up. The median is probably a better estimator of the "average".

13. There are many right answers; one is $-20, 4, 6, 10$.

15. (a) and (d)

Section 3.4: Exercises

1. Mean, median, quartile and percentile are not measures of variation.

3. Both b and c are true. The std. dev. is 0 only when all values are the same; the mean and median are therefore also that same value.

5. d, as very young and very old people may be in attendance.

7. b, Standard Deviation

9. b, You made a mistake in your calculation. The standard deviation cannot be negative.

11. d, 19.1

13. c, 17.3

15. c, $15 = 75 - 60$

17. Skewed Left

19. A

21.

Section 3.5: Exercises

1. b, the output is a height, the 78th percentile of the data set.

3. c, the output is a height, the median of the data set.

5. 50%

7. b, it would increase to a value greater than $35,000.

9. c, Yes, because a smaller standard deviation means there are fewer people with an IQ above Jeremy's.

11. The worksheet `VS_RelativeStanding2_Prob&Sol` also contains the solution.

Section 4.1: Exercises

1. $P(C) = 0.0028$

3. a, The probability is 4/39

5. 0.68

7. 1

9. 0.005

Section 4.2: Exercises

1. 0.53

3. Range of 1,075 and 1,575 people.

Section 4.3: Exercises

1. Increase

3. Decrease

5. (a) $11/30 = 0.3367$

   (b) The confidence interval is $(0.222, 0.511)$.

   (c) 63 to 270 students

7. Yes at each of the 90%, 95%, and 99% confidence levels, as each confidence interval does not include 0.5, or 50%.

9. (a) 601

   (b) Approximately 782.

11. b, No, this is a population proportion and not a sample. We do not need to use an estimate.

Section 4.4: Exercises

1. a, d, g: sample standard deviation, sample size, appropriate t-value

3. (a) The confidence interval is $(3.12, 5.61)$.

   (b) The confidence interval is $(6.31, 11.84)$.

   (c) i, Yes, the entire confidence interval for the lozenge group is below the confidence interval for the placebo group.

5. c, A 90% confidence interval for the proportion of clinical trial participants who lost more than 30 lbs in 6 months.

Section 4.5: Exercises

1. a and c

3. True

5. a, Reject the null hypothesis.

Section 4.6: Exercises

1. a, c, e

3. a, c

5. (a) Is the average income of those with a high school education less than the average income of those with a 4-year college degree?

   (b) iii, $H_0 : \mu_1 \geq \mu_2$

   (c) i, $H_0 : \mu_1 < \mu_2$

7. Let p_1 and p_2 be the home winning proportion for the basketball and lacrosse teams, respectively.

   $H_0 : p_1 = p_2$

   (b) $H_1 : p_1 \neq p_2$

   (c) The P-value is not less than the significant level; $0.974 > 0.05$. Therefore we fail to reject the null hypothesis.

(d) There is insufficient evidence to conclude the home winning proportions of the two teams are different.

Section 4.7: Exercises

1. It cannot be determined with the information provided. In order to conclude that the result is statistically significant, you need to know a P-value.

3. Is the proportion of baby girls born using the YSORT procedure greater than 0.5?

5. a, p = Proportion of baby girls

7. c, $H_1 : p > 0.5$

9. Fail to reject the null hypothesis

11. Is the average annual income of those with a high school education less than the average annual income of those with a college degree?

13. c, μ_1 = Mean income of high school graduates & μ_2 = Mean income of college graduates

15. a, $H_1 : \mu_1 < \mu_2$

17. Reject the null hypothesis.

Section 4.8: Exercises

1. $52.5138 = 182 \times 73/253$

3. b, H_1: The success of the treatment is dependent of the type of treatment.

5.

47.5	18.5
66.2	25.8
52.5	20.5
15.8	6.2

7. d, We reject the null hypothesis. The success is dependent on the treatment type.

Made in the USA
Middletown, DE
11 August 2023

36534003R00144